STUDENT UNIT GUIDE

NEW EDITION

Edexcel AS Biology Unit 1
Lifestyle, Transport, Genes and Health

Mary Jones

PHILIP ALLAN

Philip Allan, an imprint of Hodder Education, an Hachette UK company, Market Place, Deddington, Oxfordshire OX15 0SE

Orders
Bookpoint Ltd, 130 Milton Park, Abingdon, Oxfordshire OX14 4SB
tel: 01235 827827
fax: 01235 400401
e-mail: education@bookpoint.co.uk
Lines are open 9.00 a.m.–5.00 p.m., Monday to Saturday, with a 24-hour message answering service. You can also order through the Philip Allan Updates website: www.philipallan.co.uk

© Mary Jones 2012

ISBN 978-1-4441-7215-7

First printed 2012
Impression number 5 4 3 2 1
Year 2017 2016 2015 2014 2013 2012

Cover photo: Fotolia

Printed in Dubai

Typeset by Greenhill Wood Studios

Hachette UK's policy is to use papers that are natural, renewable and recyclable products and made from wood grown in sustainable forests. The logging and manufacturing processes are expected to conform to the environmental regulations of the country of origin.

Contents

Content Guidance

Questions & Answers

Getting the most from this book

Questions & Answers

Exam-style questions

Examiner comments on the questions
Tips on what you need to do to gain full marks, indicated by the icon ⊜.

Sample student answers
Practise the questions, then look at the student answers that follow each set of questions.

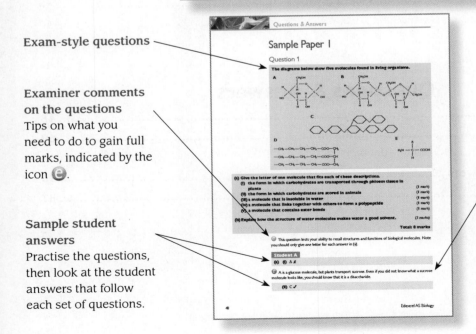

Examiner commentary on sample student answers
Find out how many marks each answer would be awarded in the exam and then read the examiner comments (preceded by the icon ⊜) following each student answer.

About this book

This book is the first in a series of four, which will help you to prepare for the Edexcel AS and A-level biology examination. It covers **Unit 1: Lifestyle, Transport, Genes and Health**. This is the first of two content-based units that make up the AS biology examination. The other three books in the series cover Units 2, 4 and 5.

This guide has two main sections:

- **Content Guidance** This provides a summary of the facts and concepts that you need to know for the Unit 1 examination.
- **Questions and Answers** This section contains two specimen papers for you to try, each worth 80 marks. There are also two sets of answers for each question, one from a candidate who is likely to get a C grade and another from a candidate who is likely to get an A grade.

The specification

It is a good idea to have your own copy of the Edexcel biology specification. It is you who is going to take this examination, not your teacher, and so it is your responsibility to make sure you know as much about the exam as possible. You can download a copy free from **www.edexcel.org.uk**.

The AS examination is made up of three units:

- Unit 1   Lifestyle, Transport, Genes and Health
- Unit 2   Development, Plants and the Environment
- Unit 3   Practical Biology and Research Skills

This book covers Unit 1, and the second book in the series covers Unit 2. There is no book for Unit 3, because this is based on practical work that you will do in your biology classes.

Unit 1 content

The content of each unit is clearly set out in the specification. Unit 1 has two topics:

- Lifestyle, health and risk
- Genes and health

Lifestyle, health and risk begins by looking at the structure of water molecules (there could be no life without water) and how their properties affect living things. This leads into the structure and functions of two other vital types of molecules: carbohydrates and triglycerides.

The cardiovascular system (heart and blood vessels) follows next, including a look at how a person's lifestyle affects cardiovascular health. Then we look at how studies have helped — and can continue to help — us to find out just what factors are important in maintaining cardiovascular health, and how we should interpret the results of such studies.

Genes and health starts with a consideration of the structure of cell membranes and how they work. Gas exchange is discussed. Then we look at another group of molecules — proteins, including those that work as enzymes. This leads us to nucleic acids (DNA and RNA) and a first look at how the DNA in our cells affects the proteins made in our cells and therefore how the cells function. (There is more about this in the A2 course.) Genetics, gene therapy and genetic screening are covered. As well as knowing some scientific facts about these, you'll need to think about moral and ethical issues relating to them.

Unit 1 assessment

Unit 1 is assessed in an examination lasting 1 hour 15 minutes. The questions are all structured — that is, they are broken up into several parts, with spaces in which you write your answers. There are 80 marks available on the paper.

What is assessed?

It's easy to forget that your examination isn't just testing what you *know* about biology — it's also testing your *skills*. It's difficult to overemphasise how important these are.

The Edexcel examination tests three different assessment objectives (AOs). The following table gives a breakdown of the proportion of marks awarded to knowledge and to skills in the AS examination:

Assessment objective	Outline of what is tested	Percentage of marks
AO1	Knowledge and understanding of science and of How Science Works	30–34
AO2	Application of knowledge and understanding of science and of How Science Works	34–40
AO3	How Science Works	28

AO1 is about remembering and understanding all the biological facts and concepts you have covered in this unit. AO2 is about being able to *use* these facts and concepts in new situations. The examination paper will include questions that contain unfamiliar contexts or sets of data, which you will need to interpret in the light of the biological knowledge you have. When you are revising, it is important that you try to develop your ability to do this, as well as just learning the facts.

AO3 is about How Science Works. Note that this comes into AO1 and AO2 as well. A science subject such as biology is not just a body of knowledge. Scientists do research to find out how things around them work, and new research continues to find out new things all the time. Sometimes new research means that we have to change our ideas. For example, not all that long ago people were encouraged to eat lots of eggs and drink lots of milk, because it was thought to be 'healthy'. Now we know we need to take care not to eat too many animal-based fats, because new research has found links between a fatty diet and heart disease.

How Science Works is about developing theories and models in biology, and testing them. It involves doing experiments to test hypotheses, and analysing the results to determine whether the hypothesis is supported or disproved. You need to appreciate why science does not always give us clear answers to the questions we ask, and how we can design good experiments whose results we can trust. You will learn about the difference between correlation and causation.

Scientific language

Throughout your biology course, and especially in your examination, it is important to use clear and correct biological language. Scientists take great care to use language precisely. If doctors or researchers do not use exactly the correct word when communicating with someone, then what they are saying could easily be misinterpreted. Biology has a huge number of specialist terms (probably more than any other subject you can choose to study at AS) and it is important that you learn them and use them. Your everyday conversational language, or what you read in the newspaper or hear on the radio, is often not the kind of language required in a biology examination. Be precise and careful in what you write, so that an examiner cannot possibly misunderstand you.

The examination

Time

You will have 75 minutes to answer questions worth 80 marks. That gives you almost 1 minute per mark. When you are trying out a test question, time yourself. Are you working too fast? Or are you taking too long? Get used to what it feels like to work at just over a-mark-a-minute rate.

It's not a bad idea to spend one of those minutes just skimming through the exam paper before you start writing. Maybe one of the questions looks as though it is going to need a bit more of your time than the others. If so, make sure you leave a little bit of extra time for it.

Read the question carefully

That sounds obvious, but candidates lose large numbers of marks by not doing it.

- There is often vital information at the start of the question that you'll need in order to answer the questions themselves. Don't just jump straight to the first place where there are answer lines and start writing. Start reading at the beginning! Examiners are usually careful not to give you unnecessary information, so if it is there it is probably needed. You may like to use a highlighter to pick out any particularly important bits of information in the question.
- Do look carefully at the command words (the ones right at the start of the question) and do what they say. For example, if you are asked to *explain* something then you won't get many marks — perhaps none at all — if you *describe* it instead. You can find all these words in an appendix near the end of the specification document.

Depth and length of answer

The examiners will give you two useful guidelines about how much you need to write.

- **The number of marks**. Obviously, the more marks the more information you need to give. If there are 2 marks, then you'll need to give two different pieces of information in order to get both of them. If there are 5 marks, you'll need to write much more.

- **The number of lines**. This isn't such a useful guideline as the number of marks, but it can still help you to know how much to write. If you find your answer won't fit on the lines, then you probably haven't focused sharply enough on the question. The best answers are short and precise.

Writing, spelling and grammar

The examiners are testing your biology knowledge and skills, not your English skills. Still, if they can't understand what you have written then they can't give you any marks. It is your responsibility to communicate clearly — don't scribble so fast that the examiner cannot read what you have written.

In general, incorrect spellings are not penalised. If the examiner knows what you are trying to say then he or she will give you credit. However, if your wrongly spelt word could be confused with another, then you won't be given the mark. For example, if you write 'meitosis', then the examiner can't know whether you mean meiosis or mitosis, so you'll be marked wrong.

Like spelling, bad grammar isn't taken into account. Once again, though, if it is so bad that the examiner cannot understand you, then you won't get marks. A common problem is to use the word 'it' in such as way that the examiner can't be certain what 'it' refers to. A good general rule is never to use this word in an exam answer.

Content Guidance

Lifestyle, health and risk

Water

About 80% of the body of an organism is water. Water has unusual properties compared with other substances, because of the structure of its molecules. Each water molecule has a small negative charge ($\delta-$) on the oxygen atom and a small positive charge ($\delta+$) on each of the hydrogen atoms. This is called a **dipole**.

There is an attraction between the $\delta-$ and $\delta+$ parts of neighbouring water molecules. This is called a **hydrogen bond**.

A single water molecule

Hydrogen bonding between water molecules

Hydrogen bond

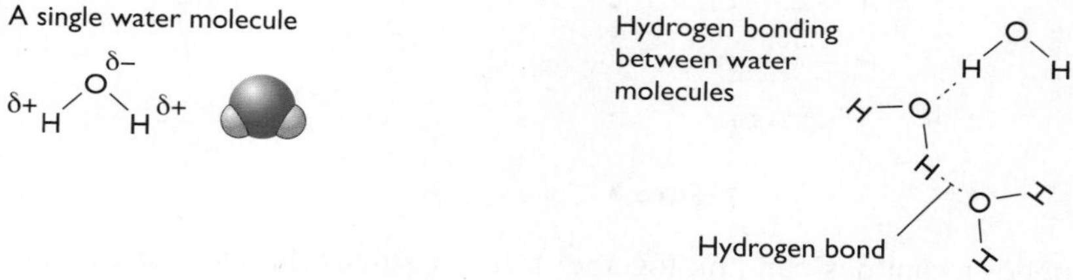

Figure 1 Water molecules

Examiner tip
The molecular formula for water, H_2O, shows that each molecule contains two hydrogen atoms bonded to one oxygen atom.

Solvent properties of water

The dipoles on water molecules make water an excellent solvent. For example, if you stir sodium chloride into water, the sodium and chloride ions separate and spread between the water molecules — they dissolve in the water. This happens because the positive charge on each sodium ion is attracted to the small negative charge on the oxygen of the water molecules. Similarly, the negative chloride ions are attracted to the small positive charge on the hydrogens of the water molecules.

Any substance that has fairly small molecules with charges on them, or that can separate into ions, can dissolve in water.

Examiner tip
The symbol for sodium is Na. The formula for a sodium ion is Na^+, showing that it has a single positive charge.

Sodium chloride crystal

Chloride ion in solution

Sodium ion in solution

Figure 2 Water as a solvent

Because it is a good solvent, water helps to transport substances around the bodies of organisms. For example, the blood plasma of mammals is mostly water, and carries many substances in solution, including glucose, oxygen and ions such as sodium.

Carbohydrates

Carbohydrates are substances whose molecules contain carbon, hydrogen and oxygen atoms, and in which there are approximately twice as many hydrogen atoms as carbon or oxygen atoms.

Monosaccharides and disaccharides

The simplest carbohydrates are monosaccharides. These are sugars. They include glucose, fructose and galactose. These each have six carbon atoms, so they are also known as hexose sugars. Their formula is $C_6H_{12}O_6$.

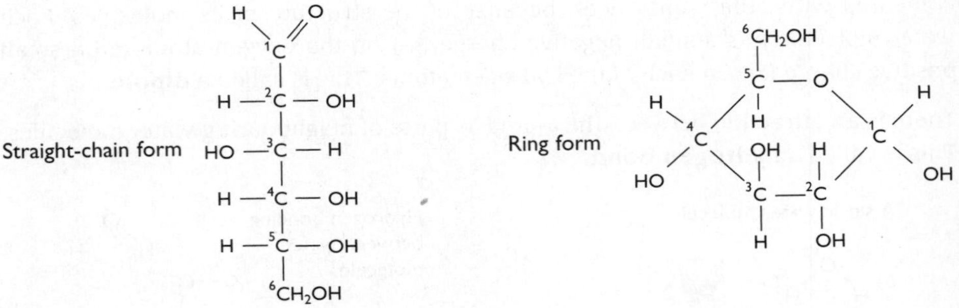

Figure 3 Glucose molecules

Two monosaccharides can link together to form a disaccharide. For example, two glucose molecules can link to produce maltose. The bond that joins them together is called a **glycosidic bond**. As the two monosaccharides react and the glycosidic bond forms, a molecule of water is released. This type of reaction is known as a **condensation** reaction. Different disaccharides can be formed by linking different monosaccharides.

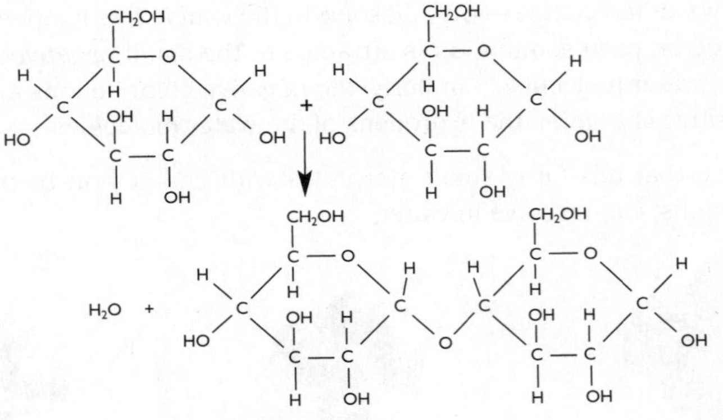

Knowledge check 1

Using the numbers in Figure 3, state the numbers of the carbon atoms involved in this glycosidic bond.

Figure 4 Formation of a disaccharide by a condensation reaction

Disaccharide	Monosaccharides which it contains
Maltose	Glucose + glucose
Lactose	Glucose + galactose
Sucrose	Glucose + fructose

Edexcel AS Biology

Disaccharides can be split apart into two monosaccharides by breaking the glycosidic bond. To do this, a molecule of water is added. This is called an **hydrolysis** reaction.

Figure 5 Breakdown of a disaccharide by an hydrolysis reaction

Monosaccharides and disaccharides are good sources of energy in living organisms. They can be used in respiration, in which the energy they contain is used to make ATP. Because they are soluble, they are the form in which carbohydrates are transported through an organism's body. In animals, glucose is transported dissolved in blood plasma. In plants, sucrose is transported in phloem sap.

Polysaccharides

These are substances whose molecules contain hundreds or thousands of monosaccharides linked together into long chains. Because their molecules are so enormous, they do not dissolve in water. This makes them good for storing energy. When needed, they can be hydrolysed to form monosaccharides, which can be used in respiration. In animals and fungi, the storage polysaccharide is **glycogen**. It is made of glucose molecules linked together. Most of the glycosidic bonds are between carbon 1 on one glucose, and carbon 4 on the next, so they are called 1–4 links. There are also some 1–6 links, which form branches in the chain.

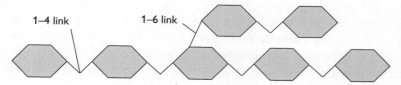

Figure 6 A small part of a glycogen molecule

In plants, the storage polysaccharide is **starch**. Starch is a mixture of two substances, **amylose** and **amylopectin**. An amylose molecule is a very long chain of glucose molecules with 1–4 links. It coils up into a spiral, making it very compact. The spiral is held in shape by hydrogen bonds between small charges on some of the hydrogen and oxygen atoms in the glucose units. An amylopectin molecule is very similar to glycogen.

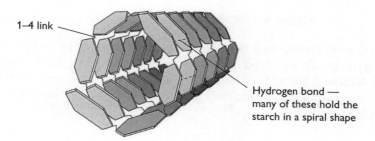

Figure 7 Part of an amylose molecule

> **Knowledge check 2**
>
> How does glycogen differ from starch?

Lipids

Lipids, like carbohydrates, also contain carbon, hydrogen and oxygen, but there is a much smaller proportion of oxygen. **Triglycerides** are an important group of lipids. Their molecules are made of a 'backbone' of **glycerol**, to which three fatty acids are attached by **ester bonds**. All lipids are insoluble in water.

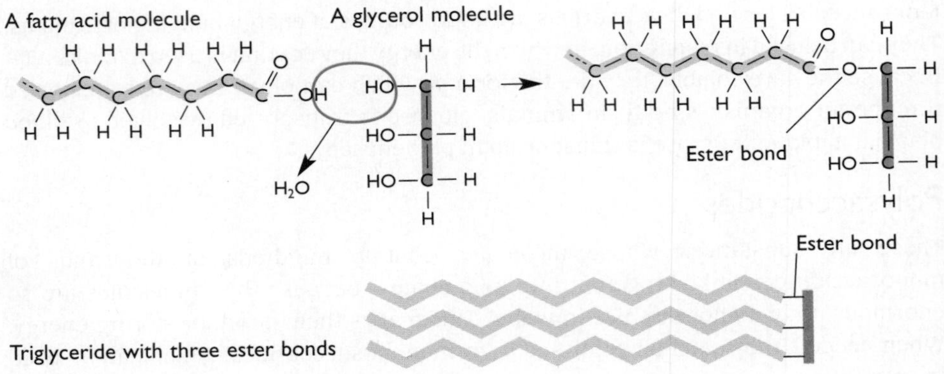

A fatty acid molecule   A glycerol molecule

Ester bond

Ester bond

Triglyceride with three ester bonds

Figure 8 The formation of a triglyceride molecule

Knowledge check 3

Look at the structure of a lipid molecule. Why is it insoluble in water?

Fatty acids have long chains made of carbon and hydrogen atoms. Each carbon atom has four bonds. Usually, two of these bonds are attached to other carbon atoms, and the other two to hydrogen atoms. In some cases, however, there may be only one hydrogen atom attached. This leaves a 'spare' bond, which attaches to the next-door carbon atom, forming a **double bond**. Fatty acids with one or more carbon–carbon double bonds are called **unsaturated** fatty acids, because they do not contain quite as much hydrogen as they could. Fatty acids with no double bonds are called **saturated** fatty acids.

Examiner tip

If you are drawing the structure of a molecule, check that you have shown four bonds on each C atom.

An unsaturated fatty acid   A saturated fatty acid

Double bond

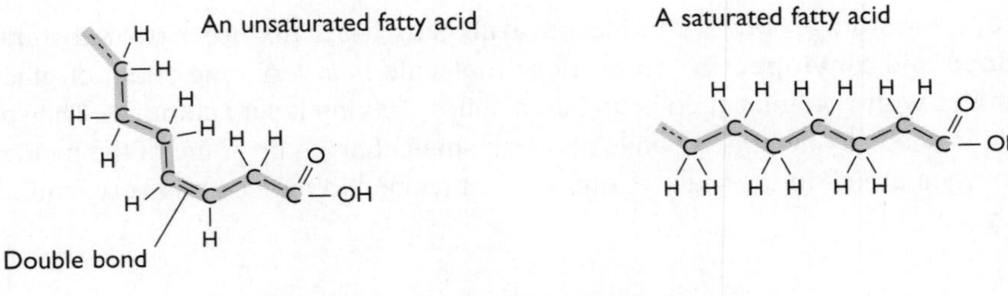

Figure 9 Unsaturated and saturated fatty acids

Lipids containing unsaturated fatty acids are called unsaturated lipids, and those containing completely saturated fatty acids are called saturated lipids. Animal lipids are often saturated lipids. They tend to be fairly solid at room temperature. Plant lipids are often unsaturated, and they tend to be oils, i.e. they are liquid at room temperature.

After studying this topic, you should be able to:
- explain why water is a good solvent, and how it is used in transport
- relate the structure of monosaccharides, disaccharides, glycogen and starch to their functions
- explain how condensation reactions and hydrolysis reactions form and break glycosidic bonds
- describe the structure of saturated and unsaturated triglycerides, and explain how ester bonds are formed and broken

The heart and circulatory system

Most living cells require supplies of oxygen and nutrients, which move into the cell through the membrane, often by diffusion. Their waste products, such as carbon dioxide, leave the cell in the same way. In a large organism, however, it would take much too long for diffusion to supply the cells that are not near the surface of the body. Diffusion is fine for very small organisms, because they have a large **surface area to volume ratio**. For larger organisms, surface area to volume ratio is much less. They need to move substances more rapidly than by diffusion, and this is generally done by **mass flow** (mass transport) of liquids. In vertebrates and many other types of animals, the liquid is blood, pumped by a heart through a series of tubes called blood vessels.

> **Examiner tip**
> Diffusion involves the random movement of individual molecules and is very slow. Mass flow is like water flowing in a river and is much faster.

The cardiac cycle

The heart of a mammal has four chambers. The two atria receive blood, and the two ventricles push blood out of the heart. The atria and ventricle on the left side of the heart contain oxygenated blood, while those on the right side contain deoxygenated blood. The walls of the heart are made of cardiac muscle.

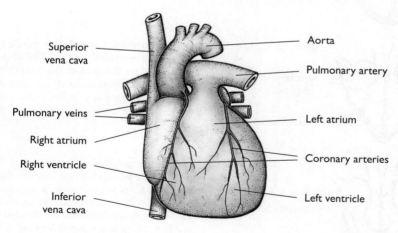

Superior vena cava · Aorta · Pulmonary artery · Pulmonary veins · Left atrium · Right atrium · Coronary arteries · Right ventricle · Inferior vena cava · Left ventricle

Figure 10 External view of a mammalian heart

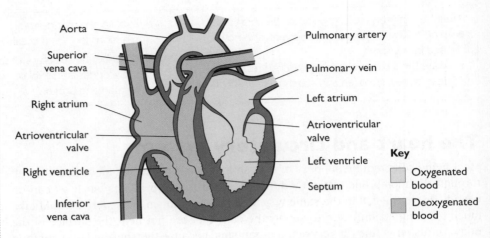

Figure 11 Vertical section through a mammalian heart

When muscle contracts, it gets shorter. Contraction of the cardiac muscle in the walls of the heart therefore causes the walls to squeeze inwards on the blood inside the heart. Both sides of the heart contract and relax together. The complete sequence of one heart beat is called the **cardiac cycle**.

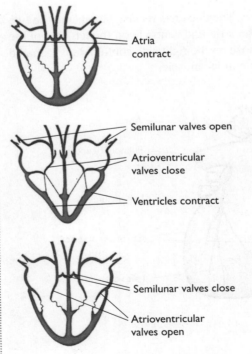

During **atrial systole**, the muscle in the walls of the atria contracts, pushing more blood into the ventricles.

During **ventricular systole**, the muscle in the walls of the ventricles contracts. This causes the pressure of the blood inside the ventricles to become greater than in the atria, forcing the atrioventricular valves shut. The blood is forced out through the aorta and pulmonary artery.

During **diastole**, the heart musles relax. The pressure inside the ventricles becomes less than inside the aorta and pulmonary artery, so the blood inside these vessels pushes the semilunar valves shut. Blood flows into the atria from the veins, so the cycle is ready to begin again.

Figure 12 The cardiac cycle

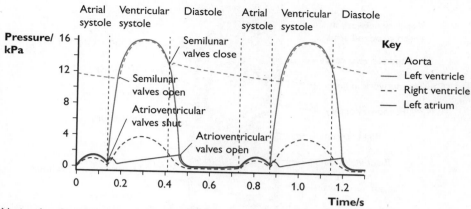

Notice that the valves open and close according to the relative pressure in the chambers that they separate. For example, when the pressure in the ventricle is greater than in the atrium, the net force of the blood is upward and this forces the atrioventricular valves shut.

Figure 13 Pressure changes during the cardiac cycle

Knowledge check 4

Using the graph, calculate the number of heart beats in one minute.

Blood vessels

Arteries carry blood away from the heart. The blood that flows through them is pulsing and at a high pressure. They therefore have thick, elastic walls which can expand and recoil as the blood pulses through. The walls also contain variable amounts of smooth muscle. They branch into smaller vessels called **arterioles**. These also contain smooth muscle in their walls, which can contract and make the lumen (space inside) smaller. This helps to control the flow of blood to different parts of the body. (Note that the muscle in the walls of arteries does not help to push the blood through them.)

Capillaries are tiny vessels with just enough space for red blood cells to squeeze through. Their walls are only one cell thick, and there are often gaps in the walls through which plasma (the liquid component of blood) can leak out. Capillaries deliver nutrients, hormones and other requirements to body cells, and take away their waste products. Their small size and thin walls minimise diffusion distance, enabling exchange to take place rapidly between the blood and the body cells.

Veins carry low-pressure blood back to the heart. Their walls do not need to be as tough or as elastic as those of arteries. The lumen is larger than in arteries, so as to reduce friction which would otherwise slow down blood movement. They contain valves, to ensure that the blood does not flow the wrong way. Blood is kept moving through many veins, for example those in the legs, by the squeezing effect produced by contraction of the body muscles close to them, which are used when walking.

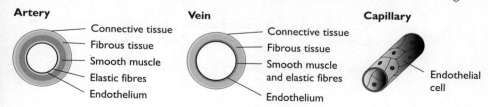

Figure 14 Structure of blood vessels

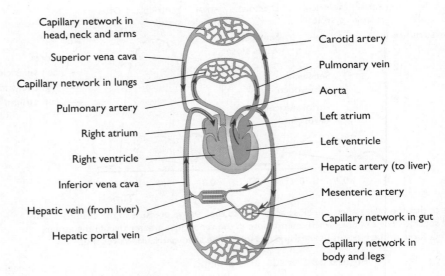

Figure 15 The main blood vessels in the human body

Pressure changes in the circulatory system

The pressure of the blood changes as it moves through the circulatory system.

- In the arteries, blood is at high pressure because it has just been pumped out of the heart. The pressure oscillates (goes up and down) in time with the heart beat. The stretching and recoil of the artery walls helps to smooth the oscillations, so the pressure becomes gradually steadier the further the blood moves along the arteries. The mean pressure also gradually decreases.
- The total cross-sectional area of the capillaries is greater than that of the arteries that supply them, so blood pressure is less inside the capillaries than inside arteries.
- In the veins, blood is at a very low pressure, as it is now a long way from the pumping effect of the heart.

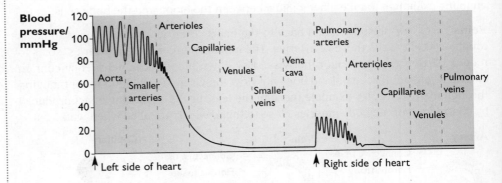

Figure 16 Pressure changes in the circulatory system

Investigating the effect of caffeine on the heart rate of *Daphnia*

Daphnia is a small, aquatic crustacean. When viewed through a microscope, the heart can be seen and the number of times it beats in 1 minute can be counted.

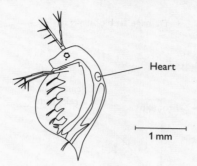

Heart

1 mm

The animal is placed in a cavity slide in a drop of water. The low power objective of a microscope is used to view it, and the number of beats in 30 seconds is counted. This can be repeated three times and an average calculated.

Using either the same *Daphnia* or a similar *Daphnia*, place an animal in a clean cavity slide. Add enough caffeine solution to immerse the *Daphnia* and count the heart rate as before. Do this for several different concentrations of caffeine. Plot mean heart rate against caffeine concentration.

Other variables, such as temperature, lighting and the conditions in which the *Daphnia* were kept before the experiment must be kept constant.

Care must be taken not to distress the animals unduly. It is generally held that it is unethical to inflict unnecessary suffering on animals. Many people do not believe that this needs to apply to invertebrates, as they believe they have no feelings or do not feel pain. However, most invertebrates do have nervous systems and probably do feel pain. Some religions ban all experimenting on animals, including invertebrates.

Blood clotting

When a blood vessel is broken or damaged, the blood inside it clots. This is important so that:

- not too much blood will be lost from the body
- pathogens (disease-causing microorganisms) cannot get in through the wound.

1 The damaged tissue in the blood vessel wall releases a mixture of substances called **thromboplastin**.
2 Blood contains little cell fragments called **platelets**. When the platelets contact the damaged tissue, they are activated. They become sticky and release **calcium ions**.
3 Blood plasma contains a soluble protein called **prothrombin**. Thromboplastin causes prothrombin to change to an enzyme called **thrombin**.

4 Blood plasma also contains a soluble protein called **fibrinogen**. In the presence of calcium ions, thrombin causes fibrinogen to change to an insoluble fibrous protein, **fibrin**.

5 Fibrin precipitates to form long fibres. Platelets and red blood cells get tangled in the fibres and form a blood clot.

Knowledge check 7

Which of the substances involved in blood clotting are proteins?

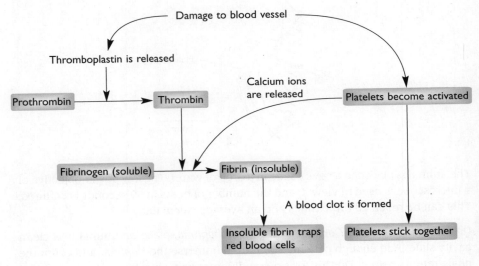

Figure 17 Blood clotting

Summary

After studying this topic, you should be able to:
- explain the difference between diffusion and mass flow, and why many animals have a heart and circulatory system
- relate the structure of the heart to its function, and describe the cardiac cycle
- name the major blood vessels, and explain how the structure of the walls of arteries, veins and capillaries are related to their functions
- describe how to investigate the effect of caffeine on the heart rate of *Daphnia*
- describe how blood clots

Cardiovascular disease

Cardiovascular disease is a term used to describe diseases of the heart and blood vessels. It is often known as **CVD**. CVD is a major cause of death in many countries, including the UK. CVD is often the result of atherosclerosis.

Atherosclerosis

Atherosclerosis is also known as 'hardening of the arteries'. It develops as the result of this sequence of events:

- The endothelium (inner layer of tissue) of an artery gets damaged and becomes rough. This happens in all of us as we age, but tends to happen earlier in people with high blood pressure. It is also caused by chemicals in cigarette smoke.
- The damaged tissues and the white cells in the blood respond to the damage by secreting several different chemicals. An **inflammatory response** takes place.
- During the inflammatory response, white blood cells crawl out of the blood and into the artery wall. **Cholesterol** from the blood also builds up in the wall, forming a deposit called an **atheroma**.
- Over time, fibrous tissue builds up around the cholesterol, forming a plaque.

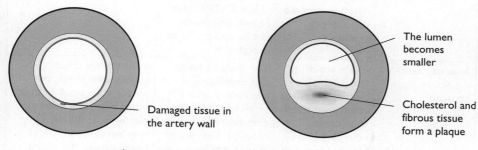

Damaged tissue in the artery wall

The lumen becomes smaller

Cholesterol and fibrous tissue form a plaque

Figure 18 Formation of plaque in an artery wall

Examiner tip
Notice that the plaque is *inside* the wall of the artery, not just stuck on its inner surface.

The plaque makes the artery wall thicker and less elastic. The artery is therefore narrower, so it is more difficult for blood to flow through it. Blood pressure increases. The high blood pressure increases the risk that more plaques will form.

The slow flow of blood past a plaque means platelets come into close contact with the damaged tissue in the vessel wall. This can stimulate a blood clot to form. When this happens inside a blood vessel, it is called a **thrombosis**. The clot can block the artery.

If a blood clot forms in a coronary artery, the flow of blood to part of the heart muscle is stopped. The muscle no longer gets a supply of oxygen and nutrients, so cannot respire aerobically. It therefore has no energy to contract and may even die. This part of the heart stops working, and the person has a **heart attack**. The severity of the attack partly depends on how much muscle is affected.

Atherosclerosis also increases the risk of **stroke** — damage to the brain caused by a burst or blocked blood vessel.

Table 1 Treatments for CVD

Treatment	How it works	Benefits	Risks
Antihypertensives	These are drugs that reduce blood pressure by affecting the sympathetic nervous system. They stop the muscles in blood vessel walls contracting.	Blood pressure is reduced. These drugs have been shown to significantly reduce death from stroke or heart disease.	• If the dosage is not correct, blood pressure may become too low (hypotension). • They also affect other functions controlled by the sympathetic nervous system, such as peristalsis in the digestive system. • Men may not be able to get an erection as this depends on raised blood pressure in the penis.
Plant statins	These are drugs that inhibit an enzyme in the liver that catalyses a reaction involved in producing cholesterol.	The concentration of cholesterol in the blood is lowered. Studies suggest that statins reduce the risk of CVD even in people who would not be thought to be at high risk.	There appear to be no risks associated with the use of statins.
Anticoagulants, e.g. warfarin, heparin	These are drugs that inhibit blood clotting. They are often prescribed to patients who have had a blood clot in a coronary artery or in the lungs.	The risk of a blood clot developing in a coronary artery or elsewhere in the circulatory system is reduced. They have saved many lives.	If the dosage is not absolutely correct, the person runs a risk of their blood not being able to clot when it should. They may increase the risk of haemorrhage (bleeding) into the brain or other parts of the body.
Platelet inhibitory drugs, e.g. aspirin	These drugs reduce the activation of platelets, so that they do not become sticky.	This reduces the risk of formation of blood clots. People are sometimes advised to take aspirin on long-distance flights, to reduce the risk of deep vein thrombosis (a clot in a leg vein).	Aspirin affects the stomach wall, making it more likely that stomach ulcers will develop in people with a tendency to this condition.

Risk factors for CVD

The following factors increase the risk that people will develop CVD:

- having genes that predispose them to it
- being overweight
- being male
- eating a high-fat diet, particularly one rich in saturated fats
- smoking cigarettes

Knowledge check 8

Explain why reducing high blood pressure reduces the risk of developing CVD.

Examiner tip

A drug is a substance that affects metabolism in the body.

Knowledge check 9

It may soon become possible to have your DNA analysed to see if you have genes increasing the risk of CVD. Suggest benefits and potential problems of this.

Edexcel AS Biology

- doing little physical exercise
- having a high ratio of LDLs to HDLs in their blood (see page 24)

The risk of developing CVD also increases with age.

Obesity indicators

People are defined as obese if their body mass index (BMI) is greater than $30\,\mathrm{kg\,m^{-2}}$. To calculate BMI, divide body mass in kg by height in metres, squared. A high BMI increases the risk of CVD.

Waist circumference can also be used to indicate obesity. A waist circumference of more than 94 cm in men and more than 80 cm in women is associated with a higher risk of CVD.

Waist-to-hip ratio is also an obesity indicator. The higher the waist-to-hip ratio, the greater the risk of CVD. This obesity indicator is the one that has the closest relationship with CVD risk. (See Figure 19 on page 23.)

Diet and energy budgets

We obtain our energy from the food that we eat. The energy content of food is measured in kilojoules, kJ. The amount of energy taken in per day should approximately equal the amount of energy used by the body. If significantly less energy is taken in, then the body will lose weight over time. If significantly more energy is taken in than is used, then the body will store the excess as fat and will gain weight over time. This is the cause of obesity. Unwanted weight gain can be stopped or reversed by increasing the amount of energy used per day, or by decreasing the amount of energy taken in.

Table 2 Energy content of nutrients

Nutrient	Energy content/kJ g^{-1}
Carbohydrate	17
Protein	17
Lipid	39
Vitamins, minerals, water	0

Different people use different amounts of energy per day, so need different amounts in their diet. It is therefore difficult to generalise about people's energy requirements. Energy needs are influenced by genes, gender and lifestyle. The table below gives a rough guide.

Table 3 Energy requirements at different stages of life

Person	Energy requirement/kJ day^{-1}
1-year-old child	4000–5000
10-year-old child	7000–8500
19-year-old	8000–10 500
Pregnant woman	8500–9500
75-year-old	7500–9000

Investigating the vitamin C content of food and drink

Vitamin C is ascorbic acid. It is an antioxidant — a chemical which 'mops up' dangerous free radicals that may be present in the body. It has been suggested that taking vitamin C supplements may help to reduce the risk of developing CVD, but several recent studies have not supported this view. However, there is good evidence that eating foods that contain antioxidants, including vitamin C, vitamin E and beta-carotene, does reduce the risk of CVD and also cancer. These nutrients are found in fresh fruit and vegetables.

The vitamin C content of a sample of drink can be measured using a reagent called DCPIP. Vitamin C causes a solution of DCPIP to lose its blue colour.

Place a measured volume of ascorbic acid solution of known concentration, $A\,\mathrm{g\,cm^{-3}}$, into a conical flask. Place DCPIP solution into a burette. Add the DCPIP solution to the ascorbic acid solution drop by drop, swirling to mix, until the blue colour of the drop does not disappear when mixed with the ascorbic acid solution. Record the volume of DCPIP solution used. Repeat three times and calculate the mean volume of DCPIP used, $B\,\mathrm{cm^3}$.

Wash out the conical flask and add a measured volume of the liquid to be tested. The calculation will be easier if you use the same volume as you used for the ascorbic acid solution. Repeat the titration described above and record the volume of DCPIP used. Repeat three times and calculate the mean volume of DCPIP used, $C\,\mathrm{cm^3}$. Concentration of ascorbic acid in drink $= A \times C \div B$

> **Knowledge check 10**
>
> $10\,\mathrm{cm^3}$ of DCPIP solution were decolorised by $100\,\mathrm{cm^3}$ of a $0.02\,\mathrm{g\,cm^{-3}}$ ascorbic acid solution, and by $250\,\mathrm{cm^3}$ of fruit juice. Calculate the concentration of vitamin C in the fruit juice.

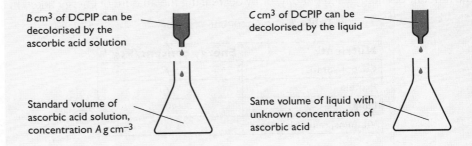

$B\,\mathrm{cm^3}$ of DCPIP can be decolorised by the ascorbic acid solution

Standard volume of ascorbic acid solution, concentration $A\,\mathrm{g\,cm^{-3}}$

$C\,\mathrm{cm^3}$ of DCPIP can be decolorised by the liquid

Same volume of liquid with unknown concentration of ascorbic acid

LDLs and HDLs

Lipids are insoluble in water, so they cannot be transported in solution in blood plasma. Instead, they are formed into little balls of protein, lipid and cholesterol called lipoproteins.

Lipoproteins containing a lot of lipids and cholesterol and a small amount of protein are called **low density lipoproteins** or **LDLs**. Lipoproteins containing a small amount of lipid and cholesterol and a lot of protein are called **high density lipoproteins** or **HDLs**.

LDLs carry lipids and cholesterol from the liver to the rest of the body. HDLs carry lipids and cholesterol from the tissues to the liver.

Relationship between cholesterol, LDLs and CVD

A high level of LDLs tends to increase the risk of developing plaques in artery walls. A high level of HDLs tends to reduce the risk.

Many different studies have shown a positive correlation between a high overall cholesterol level and the development of atheromatous plaques and CVD. There is a similar correlation between high LDL:HDL ratio and the development of atheromatous plaques and CVD.

Determining risk

It is not easy to find out exactly how particular factors affect the risk of developing CVD or other conditions. This is because we cannot do experiments on people that would be unethical. For example, a controlled experiment to investigate the hypothesis that smoking increases the risk of CVD would involve using a large group of people who were all matched for age, gender and lifestyle. The group would be split into two. The people in one group would smoke all their lives and the other group would not. If the hypothesis were correct, then people in the smoking group would, on average, develop CVD earlier, or more of them would develop CVD, than in the other group.

This kind of controlled experiment has been done on beagle dogs, but the results might not be applicable to humans. Today, it is considered unethical to carry out such experiments on animals.

Investigations into risk factors therefore generally involve recording information about a large number of people and then keeping records of their health over a period of many years. For example, a study took place in Australia in which 9206 people took part. For each person, the following was recorded in 1989:

- height and body mass, allowing BMI to be calculated (an obesity indicator)
- waist measurement was recorded, and also the ratio of waist:hip measurement (obesity indicators)
- gender and age
- whether or not they smoked

Of these 9206 subjects, 473 had died by the end of 2000. The cause of death was recorded. Statistical analysis was then carried out to see if there was any correlation between any of the factors measured and the cause of death. The graphs show some of the results for three factors.

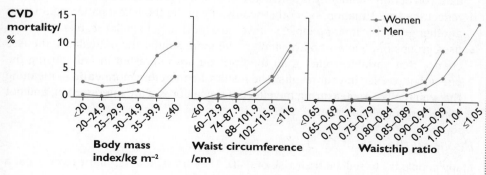

Figure 19 Obesity indicators and risk of death from CVD

Correlation and causation

All the results displayed in the graphs above show some **correlation** between the measured factor and the risk of developing CVD. The one with the closest correlation is waist:hip ratio.

However, this does not show that having a high waist:hip ratio actually *causes* CVD. To establish that one factor actually causes another, we have to do an experiment in which we purposefully alter one variable while keeping all others constant.

For example, several studies have been carried out in which people were given statins, which are known to reduce both total blood cholesterol and LDL:HDL ratio. They were matched with a similar group of people who were not given statins. The graph below shows the combined results of several of these studies. This strongly suggests that having a high LDL:HDL ratio causes the development of CVD.

Knowledge check 11

Explain the difference between correlation and causation.

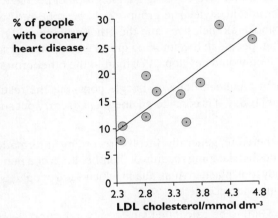

Figure 20 Combined results of several different studies into the effect of lowering LDL cholesterol on CVD events (heart attacks or strokes)

Designing a good study

Not all such experiments have been well designed, which partly explains why we do not always see similar results. A well-designed study:

- uses a large number of people. The larger the sample size, the more **reliable** the data you obtain. Reliability is a measure of how likely it is that the results really do reflect the true situation — in other words, if you did the investigation again with another group of similar people, you would expect to get similar results.
- uses groups of people who are similar. The more similar the individuals, the less chance that variables other than the one you are interested in are causing the effect that you see in your results. The results are therefore more **valid** — meaning that you really are measuring the effect of the factor you are interested in, and not something else altogether.

Reducing the risk of CVD

Many people try to reduce their risk of CVD. They try to take regular exercise, eat a balanced diet, avoid smoking and keep their weight down.

However, despite our knowledge of the factors that increase the risk of CVD, many people continue to lead lifestyles that increase their risk of developing this disease. There are many reasons for this. They include:

- confusion. As new evidence is found, earlier ideas about risk factors may be superseded by new ones. Changes like this can lead some people to distrust advice given by health professionals or the government.
- poor perception of risk. People frequently underestimate the degree to which their lifestyle increases their risk of dying from CVD.
- ignoring risk. People may push knowledge of risk to the back of their mind, preferring to live for the present rather than worry about the future.
- a feeling that nothing can be done. People may use the fact that genes have an effect on your risk of developing CVD to convince themselves that just changing their lifestyle will not have any effect.
- peer pressure. People may want to continue smoking because it helps them to fit in, or because it helps them to manage stress, or because they are addicted to nicotine.

After studying this topic, you should be able to:
- explain the course of events leading to atherosclerosis, list the factors that increase the risk of developing cardiovascular disease (CVD) and discuss the drugs that are used in treating CVD
- discuss the difference between correlation and causation, and describe the evidence for a causal

relationship between blood cholesterol levels (including HDLs and LDLs) and CVD
- describe how to investigate the vitamin C content of food and drink
- analyse data and evaluate studies investigating possible causal relationships between risk factors and illness

Summary

Genes and health

Cell membranes

Every cell is surrounded by a cell membrane. There are also many membranes within cells. The membrane around the outside of a cell is called the cell surface membrane or plasma membrane.

Structure of a cell membrane

A cell membrane consists of a double layer of **phospholipid molecules**. These are lipids with a backbone of glycerol, two fatty acid chains and a phosphate group.

The fatty acid chains have no electrical charge and so are not attracted to the dipoles of water molecules. They are said to be **hydrophobic**.

The phosphate group has an electrical charge and is attracted to water molecules. It is **hydrophilic**.

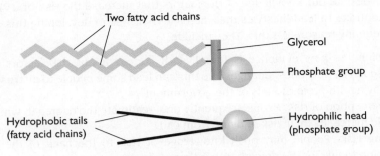

Figure 21 Phospholipids

In water, a group of phospholipid molecules arranges itself into a bilayer, with the hydrophilic heads facing outwards into the water and the hydrophobic tails facing inwards, therefore avoiding contact with water.

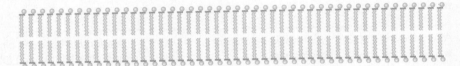

Figure 22 A phospholipid bilayer

This is the basic structure of a cell membrane. There are also **cholesterol** molecules in among the phospholipids. **Protein** molecules float in the phospholipid bilayer.

Many of the phospholipids and proteins have short chains of carbohydrates attached to them, on the outer surface of the membrane. They are known as **glycolipids** and **glycoproteins**.

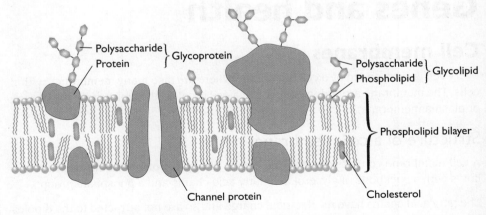

Figure 23 The fluid mosaic model of membrane structure

This is called the **fluid mosaic model** of membrane structure:

- 'fluid' because the molecules within the membrane can move around within their own layers
- 'mosaic' because the protein molecules are dotted around within the membrane

- 'model' because no-one has ever seen a membrane looking like the diagram — the molecules are too small to see, even with the most powerful microscope. The structure has been worked out because it explains the behaviour of membranes that has been discovered through experiment.

Passive transport through cell membranes

Molecules and ions are in constant motion. In gases and liquids they move freely. As a result of their random motion, each type of molecule or ion tends to spread out evenly within the space available. This is **diffusion**. Diffusion results in the net movement of particles from a high concentration to a low concentration.

Diffusion across a cell membrane

Some molecules and ions are able to pass through cell membranes. The membrane is **permeable** to these substances. However, some substances cannot pass through cell membranes, so the membranes are said to be **partially permeable**.

For example, oxygen is often in a higher concentration outside a cell than inside, because the oxygen inside the cell is being used up in respiration. The random motion of oxygen molecules inside and outside the cell means that some of them 'hit' the cell membrane. Oxygen molecules are small and do not carry an electrical charge. They are therefore able to pass freely through the phospholipid bilayer. Oxygen therefore diffuses from outside the cell, through the membrane, to the inside of the cell, down its concentration gradient.

This is called **passive** transport, because the cell does not do anything to cause the oxygen to move across the cell membrane.

Facilitated diffusion

Ions or electrically charged molecules are not able to diffuse through the phospholipid bilayer, because they are repelled from the hydrophobic tails. Large molecules are also unable to move through it freely. However, the cell membrane has special protein molecules which provide hydrophilic passageways through which these ions and molecules can pass. They are called **channel proteins**. Different channel proteins allow the passage of different types of molecules and ions. Diffusion through these channel proteins is called **facilitated diffusion**. Like 'ordinary' diffusion, it is entirely passive.

Examiner tip
Remember that diffusion is the result of completely random movement of particles. The particles do not move purposefully in a particular direction.

Knowledge check 13
Explain how breathing movements increase the rate of diffusion of carbon dioxide from the blood to the alveoli.

Examiner tip
Diffusion and facilitated diffusion result in movement *down* a concentration gradient, not 'along' it.

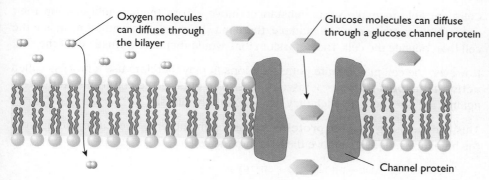

Figure 24 Diffusion across a cell membrane

Osmosis

Water molecules are small. They carry small charges (dipoles) but are still able to move quite freely through the phospholipid bilayer of cell membranes. Water molecules therefore tend to diffuse down their 'concentration gradient' across cell membranes.

Cell membranes always have a watery solution on each side. These solutions may have different concentrations of solutes.

The greater the concentration of solute, the less water is present. The water molecules in a concentrated solution are also less free to move, because they are attracted to the solute molecules (Figure 25). Water molecules in the dilute solution are moving more freely and therefore hit the membrane more often than water molecules in the concentrated solution.

More water molecules therefore diffuse across the membrane from the dilute to the concentrated solution than in the other direction.

This is **osmosis**. Osmosis is the diffusion of water molecules from a dilute solution to a concentrated solution through a partially permeable membrane.

> **Examiner tip**
> Remember that osmosis is a result of the random movement of *water* molecules.

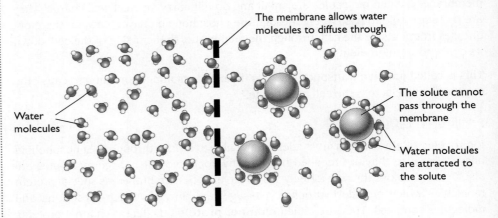

Figure 25 Osmosis across a cell membrane

Active transport across cell membranes

Cells are able to make some substances move across their membranes up their concentration gradients. For example, there may be more potassium ions inside the cell than outside the cell. The potassium ions would therefore diffuse out of the cell.

However, the cell may require potassium ions. It may therefore use a process called **active transport** to move potassium ions from outside the cell to inside the cell, against the direction in which they would naturally diffuse.

This is done using **carrier proteins** in the cell membrane. These use energy from the breakdown of ATP to move the ions into the cell.

$$ATP \longrightarrow ADP + phosphate + energy$$

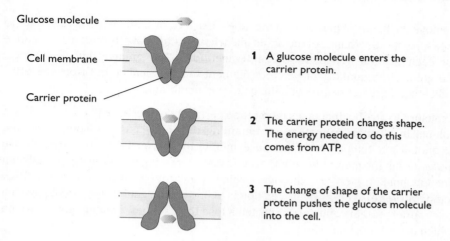

1 A glucose molecule enters the carrier protein.

2 The carrier protein changes shape. The energy needed to do this comes from ATP.

3 The change of shape of the carrier protein pushes the glucose molecule into the cell.

Figure 26 Active transport

Each carrier protein is specific to just one type of ion or molecule. Cells contain many different carrier proteins in their membranes.

Endocytosis and exocytosis

Cells can move substances into and out of the cell without the substances having to pass through the cell membrane.

In **endocytosis**, the cell puts out extensions around the object to be engulfed. The membrane fuses together around the object, forming a **vacuole**.

In **exocytosis**, the object is surrounded by a membrane inside the cell to form a vacuole or vesicle. This is then moved to the cell membrane. The membrane of the vacuole or vesicle fuses with the cell membrane, expelling its contents outside the cell.

Knowledge check 14

Suggest whether endocytosis and exocytosis require input of energy from the cell. Explain your answer.

Investigating the effect of alcohol or temperature on membrane permeability

Beetroot cells contain a red pigment which cannot pass through the cell membrane. If the structure of the membrane is damaged, the pigment can leak out. By measuring how much pigment leaks out in a particular length of time, the degree of damage to the membrane can be assessed.

Use a cork borer to cut several cylinders of beetroot, preferably all from the same root. Cut each cylinder into several smaller pieces, all exactly the same size. Wash all of them thoroughly in distilled water, to remove any red pigment from cells that have been cut open.

Prepare tubes containing different concentrations of alcohol, or containing water at different temperatures. If possible, use three tubes for each alcohol concentration or temperature. Keep all other variables constant, for example the volume of the liquid. Immerse pieces of beetroot into each tube. Leave for a standard amount of time.

Remove the beetroot pieces from the tubes. Use a colorimeter with a green filter to measure the absorbance of the liquid in each tube. Calculate the mean absorbance for each alcohol concentration or temperature. The greater the absorbance, the greater the quantity of beetroot pigment that has leaked out from the cells, indicating a greater degree of damage to the membrane.

Exposure to alcohol increases membrane permeability because phospholipids are soluble in alcohol, so instead of remaining in a bilayer they disperse into the alcohol. High temperatures increase membrane permeability because all the molecules in the membrane move around faster, creating temporary gaps between phospholipid molecules through which other molecules can pass. High temperatures also break hydrogen bonds in protein molecules (Figure 31, page 33) so channel proteins and carrier proteins lose their shapes, creating gaps through which other molecules can pass.

Knowledge check 15

Sketch a graph to predict the results of an experiment to investigate the effect of temperature on membrane permeability. Label each axis fully.

Gas exchange surfaces

All organisms need to take in substances from their environment and give out others. Some of these are gases. For example, in aerobic respiration oxygen is taken in and carbon dioxide is given out. The take-up of oxygen into an organism's body from its environment, and the loss of carbon dioxide to the environment, is an example of **gas exchange**.

In a small organism, such as a single-celled *Amoeba*, gas exchange takes place across the cell surface membrane. Both oxygen and carbon dioxide can diffuse freely through the phospholipid bilayer.

In larger organisms, the smaller surface area:volume ratio means that diffusion across the body surface would not supply oxygen fast enough for all the cells in the body. They therefore often have specialised areas of their body, in contact with their environment, in which the surface area is greatly increased. These specialised areas are called **gas exchange surfaces**.

Properties of gas exchange surfaces

- They must have a large surface area, so that many molecules of gases can move across them at the same time.
- They must be thin, so that gases can diffuse across them quickly.
- They must be provided with a good supply of air containing oxygen (or, in an aquatic organism, water containing dissolved oxygen).
- The oxygen must be taken away rapidly from the surface, for example by the flow of blood.

These last two points help to maintain a concentration gradient for oxygen across the gas exchange surface. The greater the concentration gradient, the more rapidly diffusion will occur. This also applies to the concentration gradient for carbon dioxide.

Mammalian lungs

In mammals, the alveoli inside the lungs are the gas exchange surface.

- All the alveoli together have a huge surface area, because there are many of them and they are very small.
- The wall of an alveolus is only one cell thick, and so is the wall of the blood capillary.
- Breathing movements constantly bring fresh air into the lungs and remove air from which oxygen has been lost, and to which carbon dioxide has been added in the alveoli.
- Oxygenated blood is taken away from the alveoli in the pulmonary veins.

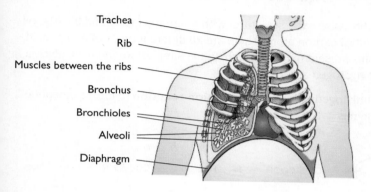

Trachea
Rib
Muscles between the ribs
Bronchus
Bronchioles
Alveoli
Diaphragm

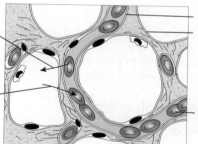

Diffusion of carbon dioxide from the blood into the alveolus

Diffusion of oxygen from the alveolus into the blood

Capillary wall (one cell thick)
Alveolus wall (one cell thick)

Red blood cell in capillary

Figure 27 Mammalian lungs

After studying this topic, you should be able to:
- describe the structure of a cell surface membrane
- explain how the properties of cell surface membranes are explained by the fluid mosaic model
- explain how passive transport — diffusion and facilitated diffusion — take place, including the role of channel proteins

- explain how active transport takes place, including the role of carrier proteins and ATP
- explain how endocytosis and exocytosis take place
- describe how to investigate membrane permeability
- explain how the structures of gas exchange surfaces, including the alveoli in mammalian lungs, are adapted to allow gas exchange to occur rapidly

Summary

Proteins

Proteins are large molecules made of long chains of **amino acids**.

Amino acids

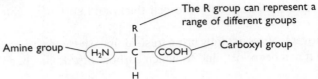

Figure 28 An amino acid

All amino acids have the same basic structure, with an amine group and a carboxyl group attached to a central carbon atom. There are 20 different types of amino acid, which differ in the atoms present in the R group. In the simplest amino acid, glycine, the R group is a single hydrogen atom.

Two amino acids can link together by a **condensation reaction** to form a dipeptide. The bond that links them is called a **peptide bond**.

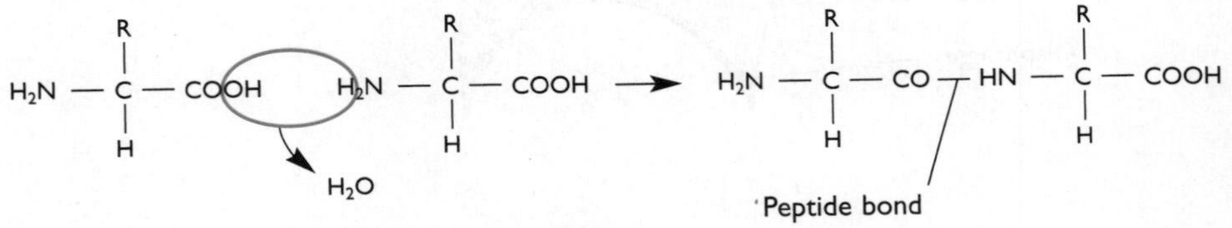

Figure 29 Formation of a dipeptide

The dipeptide can be broken down in a hydrolysis reaction, which breaks the peptide bond with the addition of a molecule of water.

Structure of protein molecules

Amino acids can be linked together in any order to form a long chain called a **polypeptide**. A polypeptide may form a protein molecule on its own, or it may associate with other polypeptide molecules to form a protein molecule.

The sequence of amino acids in a polypeptide or protein molecule is called its **primary structure**.

Val – Leu – Ser – Pro – Ala – Asp – Lys – Thr – Asn – Val – Lys – Ala

Figure 30 Primary structure

The chain of amino acids often folds or curls up on itself. For example, many polypeptide chains coil into a regular shape called an **alpha helix**. This is held in shape by hydrogen bonds between amino acids at different places in the chain. This regular shape is an example of **secondary structure** of a protein.

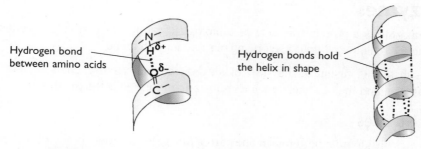

Figure 31 An alpha helix — an example of secondary structure

The polypeptide chain may also fold around on itself to form a three-dimensional shape. This is called the **tertiary structure** of the protein. Once again, hydrogen bonds between amino acids at different points in the chain help to hold it in its particular 3D shape. There are also other bonds involved, including strong **ionic bonds**, **disulfide bonds** and **hydrophobic interactions**.

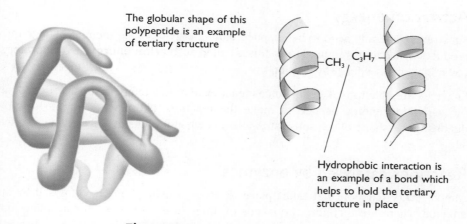

The globular shape of this polypeptide is an example of tertiary structure

Hydrophobic interaction is an example of a bond which helps to hold the tertiary structure in place

Figure 32 Tertiary structure of a protein

The tertiary structure of a protein, and therefore its properties, is ultimately determined by its primary structure.

Globular and fibrous proteins

Globular proteins have molecules that fold into a roughly spherical three-dimensional shape. Examples include haemoglobin, insulin and enzymes. They are often soluble in water and may be physiologically active — that is, they are involved in metabolic reactions within or outside cells.

Fibrous proteins have molecules that do not curl up into a ball. They have long, thin molecules, which often lie side by side to form fibres. Examples include keratin (in hair) and collagen (in skin and bone). They are not soluble in water and are not generally physiologically active. They often have structural roles.

Enzymes

An **enzyme** is a protein that acts as a biological catalyst — that is, it speeds up a metabolic reaction without itself being permanently changed.

The substance present at the start of an enzyme-catalysed reaction is called the **substrate**, and the new substance (or substances) formed is the **product**.

Active sites

Enzymes are globular proteins. In one part of the molecule, there is an area called the **active site**, where the substrate molecule can bind. The 3D shape of the active site fits the substrate perfectly, so only one type of substrate can bind with the enzyme. The enzyme is therefore **specific** for that substrate.

The R groups of the amino acids at the active site are able to form temporary bonds with the substrate molecule. This pulls the substrate molecule slightly out of shape, causing it to react and form products.

Activation energy

Substrates generally need to be supplied with energy to cause them to change into products. The energy required to do this is called **activation energy**. In a laboratory, you might supply energy by heating to cause two substances to react together.

Enzymes are able to make substances react even at low temperatures. They reduce the activation energy needed to make the reaction take place. They do this by distorting the shape of the substrate molecule when it binds at the enzyme's active site.

Knowledge check 18

High temperatures break hydrogen bonds. Explain how this will affect enzyme activity.

Reactions catalysed by enzymes

Almost every reaction that takes place in an organism's body is catalysed by an enzyme. There are therefore thousands of different enzymes, each catalysing just one type of reaction. Some of these reactions are **intracellular** (take place inside cells) while others are **extracellular** (take place outside cells).

Table 4 Some examples of reactions catalysed by enzymes

Enzyme	Substrate	Product	Examples of where the reaction takes place
Amylase	Starch	Maltose	Extracellularly, in the mouth and duodenum of mammals; also intracellularly in germinating seeds of plants
Catalase	Hydrogen peroxide	Oxygen and water	Intracellularly, in most living cells
DNA polymerase	DNA nucleotides	DNA polynucleotides	Intracellularly, in cell nuclei
ATPase	ATP	ADP and inorganic phosphate	Intracellularly, in all living cells, for example in active transport

Investigating the properties of enzymes

When an enzyme solution is added to a solution of its substrate, the random movements of enzyme and substrate molecules cause them to collide with each other. The more concentrated the enzyme or the substrate, the more frequent the collisions, and therefore the greater the rate of the reaction.

As time passes, the quantity of substrate decreases, because it is being changed into product. This decrease in substrate concentration means that the rate of the reaction gradually slows down. The reaction rate is fastest right at the start of the reaction, when substrate concentration is greatest.

When comparing reaction rates of an enzyme in different circumstances, we should therefore try to measure the *initial* rate of reaction — that is, the rate of reaction close to the start of the reaction.

Investigating the effect of enzyme concentration on rate of reaction

You could use the following method to investigate the effect of enzyme concentration on the rate at which the enzyme catalase converts its substrate, hydrogen peroxide, to water and oxygen.

Prepare a catalase solution by liquidising some biological material, such as a handful of celery stalks. This will liberate catalase from the cells. Filter the mixture. The filtrate will contain catalase in solution.

Prepare different dilutions of this solution — for example:

Volume of initial solution/cm^3	Volume of distilled water added/cm^3	Relative concentration of catalase (as a percentage of the concentration of the initial solution)
10	0	100
9	1	90
8	2	80

The final 'solution' prepared should be 10 cm^3 of distilled water.

Place each solution into a tube fitted with a gas syringe. Use relatively small tubes, so that there is not too much gas in the tube above the liquid, but leave space to add an equal volume of hydrogen peroxide solution at the next step. Ensure that each tube is labelled with waterproof marker. If time and materials allow, prepare three sets of these solutions.

Place each tube in a water bath at 30°C.

Take another set of tubes, and add 10 cm^3 of hydrogen peroxide solution to each one. The concentration of hydrogen peroxide must be the same in each tube. Stand these tubes in the same water bath.

Leave all the tubes for at least 5 minutes to allow them to come to the correct temperature.

When ready, add the contents of one of the hydrogen peroxide tubes to the first enzyme tube. Mix thoroughly. Measure the volume of gas collected in the gas syringe after two minutes. If you are using three sets, then repeat using the other two tubes containing the same concentration of enzyme.

Knowledge check 19

Sketch a curve to predict the results of this investigation.

Do the same for each of the tubes of enzyme. Record the mean volume of gas produced in 2 minutes for each enzyme concentration and plot a line graph to display your results.

Summary

After studying this topic, you should be able to:
- describe the structure of an amino acid, and explain how they link together by the formation of peptide bonds
- explain how a protein's primary structure determines its three-dimensional structure
- describe the types of bonds involved in the three-dimensional structure of a protein molecule
- explain the differences between globular and fibrous proteins, and give examples of them
- explain how enzymes act as biological catalysts, with reference to activation energy and active sites
- describe how to investigate the effect of enzyme concentration on rate of reaction, by measuring the initial rate of reaction

Polynucleotides

Polynucleotides are substances whose molecules are made of long chains of **nucleotides** linked together. DNA and RNA are polynucleotides.

A nucleotide is made up of:

Examiner tip
Take care not to confuse adenine with adenosine, or thymine with thiamine.

- a 5-carbon sugar (deoxyribose in DNA; ribose in RNA)
- a phosphate group
- a nitrogen-containing base (adenine, guanine, cytosine or thymine in DNA; adenine, guanine, cytosine or uracil in RNA)

The bases are usually referred to by their first letters, A, G, C, T and U.

A and G are **purine** bases, made up of two carbon-nitrogen rings. C, T and U are **pyrimidine** bases, made up of one carbon-nitrogen ring.

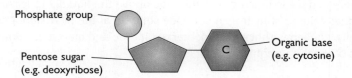

Figure 33 A nucleotide

Nucleotides can link together by the formation of covalent bonds between the phosphate group of one and the sugar of another. This takes place through a condensation reaction.

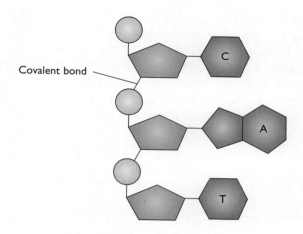

Covalent bond

Figure 34 Part of a polynucleotide

An RNA molecule is usually made up of a single strand, although this may be folded up on itself. A DNA molecule is made up of two strands, held together by hydrogen bonds between the bases on the two strands. The strands run in opposite directions, i.e. they are anti-parallel.

Hydrogen bonding only occurs between A and T and between C and G. This is called **complementary base pairing**.

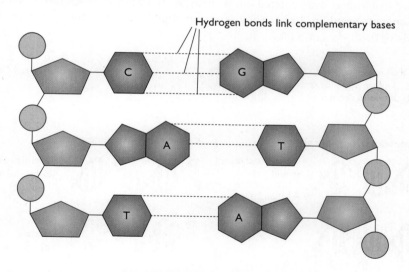

Hydrogen bonds link complementary bases

Figure 35 Part of a DNA molecule

The two strands of nucleotides twist round each other to produce a **double helix**.

DNA replication

New DNA molecules need to be made before a cell can divide. The two daughter cells must each receive a complete set of DNA. The base sequences on the new DNA molecules must be identical with those on the original set. DNA replication takes place in the nucleus.

Knowledge check 20
List *three* differences between RNA and DNA.

Examiner tip
Notice that there are three hydrogen bonds between C and G, and two between A and T.

- Hydrogen bonds between the bases along part of the two strands are broken. This 'unzips' part of the molecule, separating the two strands.
- Nucleotides that are present in solution in the nucleus are moving randomly around. By chance, a free nucleotide will bump into a newly exposed one with which it can form hydrogen bonds. Free nucleotides therefore pair up with the nucleotides on each of the DNA strands, always A with T and C with G.
- DNA polymerase links together the phosphate and deoxyribose groups of adjacent nucleotides.

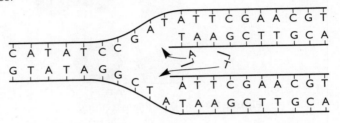

Figure 36 DNA replication

This is called **semi-conservative** replication, because each new DNA molecule has one old strand and one new one.

Meselson and Stahl's experiment

A classic experiment was carried out in 1958 by two American scientists, Matthew Meselson and Franklin Stahl. They were attempting to find out which of these methods of DNA replication took place:

Parent DNA molecule, used as a source of information for the synthesis of two molecules

Newly synthesised DNA

Semi-conservative replication

Newly synthesised strand

Old strand inherited from parent

Conservative replication

Boths strands newly synthesised

Both strands inherited from parent

They grew bacteria, *Escherichia coli*, in a medium containing ammonium chloride in which the nitrogen atoms were a heavy isotope called ^{15}N. The bacteria used this nitrogen to make the bases to synthesise new DNA molecules. They were kept on this medium for many generations, until practically all of the nitrogen in their DNA was ^{15}N.

Some of these bacteria were then moved to a different medium in which all the nitrogen was the more usual, less heavy isotope ^{14}N. The bacteria used this when making new DNA. They were left for just long enough for them to replicate their DNA once. Then some of them were removed and their DNA extracted.

DNA from the bacteria growing on the ^{15}N medium, and DNA from the bacteria that had replicated their DNA once in the ^{14}N medium, was then centrifuged in tubes containing a calcium chloride solution. The heavier the DNA, the closer to the bottom of the tube it ended up. These were the results.

DNA containing all ^{15}N

DNA after one replication in ^{14}N

The DNA made using ^{14}N was not as heavy as DNA made using ^{15}N, and so did not settle as low in the centrifuge tube. This lighter DNA was all in one band, suggesting all the DNA molecules were approximately the same weight. If replication was conservative, there would have been one band in the same position as in the first tube (all heavy) and another higher up the tube (all light). So these results suggested that semi-conservative replication, not conservative replication, had taken place.

DNA was then extracted from bacteria that had grown in the ^{14}N medium for another generation, so that one more round of DNA replication had taken place. This was done again for the next generation. These were the results.

Results after two generations in ^{14}N

Results after three generations in ^{14}N

The genetic code

The sequence of bases in a DNA molecule is a code that determines the sequence in which amino acids are linked together when making a protein molecule. A length of DNA that codes for one polypeptide, or for one protein, is known as a **gene**.

As we have seen, the sequence of amino acids in a protein — its primary structure — determines its three-dimensional shape and therefore its properties and functions.

A series of three bases in a DNA molecule, called a base **triplet**, codes for one amino acid. The triplets do not overlap. For example, this is the sequence of amino acids coded for by a particular length of DNA:

Bases in DNA   T A C C T G C A T C T T

Amino acid in polypeptide   methionine aspartate valine glutamate

There are 20 amino acids. Because there are four bases, there are $4^3 = 64$ different possible combinations of bases in a triplet. Some amino acids therefore are coded for

by more than one triplet. For example, the triplets AAA and AAG both code for the amino acid phenylalanine. The code is therefore said to be **degenerate**.

Protein synthesis

Proteins are made on the **ribosomes** in the cytoplasm, by linking together amino acids through peptide bonds. The sequence in which the amino acids are linked is determined by the sequence of bases on a length of DNA in the nucleus.

1 In the nucleus, this part of the DNA molecule unzips, exposing unpaired bases on both strands.
2 Free RNA nucleotides pair up with the bases on one of the strands (known as the **template** or **antisense** strand), by **complementary base pairing**:

DNA base	RNA base that pairs with it
A	U
T	A
C	G
G	C

A set of three bases on an RNA molecule corresponding to a triplet of bases on the DNA molecule is called a **codon**.
3 The enzyme RNA polymerase links the RNA nucleotides together to produce a messenger RNA (**mRNA**) molecule.

Steps 1, 2 and 3 are called **transcription**.

4 The mRNA molecule moves out into the cytoplasm and attaches to a ribosome.
5 Transfer RNA (**tRNA**) molecules in the cytoplasm become attached to amino acids. Each tRNA has a sequence of three unpaired bases, and this determines the particular amino acid to which it is attached. These three unpaired bases are called an **anticodon**.
6 One by one, the anticodons of tRNA molecules temporarily pair up with their complementary codons on the mRNA molecule. This brings their amino acids close together, so that they can be linked by condensation reactions.

Steps 4, 5 and 6 are called **translation**.

Mutation

A mutation is a random, unpredictable change in the DNA in a cell. It may be:

- a change in the sequence of bases in one part of a DNA molecule, or
- an addition of extra DNA to a chromosome, or a loss of DNA from it, or
- a change in the total number of chromosomes in a cell

Mutations are most likely to occur during DNA replication, for example when a 'wrong' base may slot into position in the new strand being built. Almost all of these mistakes are immediately repaired by enzymes, but some may persist.

A change in the sequence of bases in DNA may result in a change in the sequence of amino acids in a protein. (Note that this does not always happen, because there is more than one triplet that codes for each amino acid, so a change in a triplet may not

Knowledge check 23

Explain how tRNA helps to ensure that the 'correct' sequence of amino acids, determined by DNA, is assembled to make a polypeptide.

change the amino acid that is coded for.) This in turn may result in a change in the 3D structure of the protein and therefore the way that it behaves.

Cystic fibrosis is a genetic condition resulting from a mutation in a gene that codes for a carrier protein called CFTR. This protein lies in the cell surface membrane of cells in many parts of the body, including the lungs, pancreas and reproductive organs. It transports chloride ions out of cells.

There are several different mutations that result in changes in the CFTR protein. Some of them involve a change in just one base in the gene coding for the CFTR protein. The commonest one, however, involves the loss of three bases from the gene, meaning that one amino acid is missed out when the CFTR protein is being made. In all cases, the protein that is made does not work properly.

Normally, chloride ions are transported out of the cells through the CFTR protein. Water follows by osmosis. When the CFTR protein is not working, this does not happen. There is therefore less water on the outer surface of the cells than there should be. The mucus that is produced in these areas therefore does not mix with water in the usual way. The mucus is thick and sticky. As a result:

- The abnormally thick mucus collects in the lungs, interfering with gas exchange and increasing the chance of bacterial infections.
- The pancreatic duct may also become blocked with sticky mucus, interfering with digestion in the small intestine.
- Reproductive passages, such as the vas deferens, may become blocked, making a person sterile.

Knowledge check 24
Explain why the loss of one amino acid can prevent a protein from working normally.

Genetics

Genes are passed from parents to offspring inside the nuclei of the gametes. The study of this process is called **genetics**.

Haploid and diploid cells

Most of the cells in the body of a plant or animal have two complete sets of chromosomes. They are said to be **diploid**. For example, in a human cell there are two complete sets of 23 chromosomes, making 46 in all. There are two chromosome 1s, two chromosome 2s and so on.

Gametes contain only one set of chromosomes, and are said to be **haploid**. For example, in a human egg or sperm there are 23 chromosomes, one chromosome 1, one chromosome 2 and so on.

Examiner tip
Different species have different numbers of chromosomes. Humans have 46; cats have 38; fig trees have 20.

Genes and alleles

The two chromosomes in a diploid cell that are similar (e.g. the two chromosome 1s) are said to be **homologous**. They each contain the same genes in the same position. This means that there are two copies of each gene in a diploid cell.

Genes often come in different forms. For example, the gene for the CFTR protein has a normal form and several different mutant forms. These different forms of a gene are called **alleles**.

Homozygote and heterozygote

An organism that has two identical alleles for a particular gene is a **homozygote**. An organism that has two different alleles for a particular gene is a **heterozygote**.

Dominant and recessive

We can use letters to represent the different alleles of a gene. For example, we could use **F** to represent the normal cystic fibrosis allele, and **f** to represent a mutant allele.

There are three possible combinations of these alleles in a diploid organism: **FF**, **Ff** or **ff**. These are the possible **genotypes** of the organism.

These different genotypes give rise to different **phenotypes** — the observable characteristics of the organism.

Genotype	Phenotype
FF	Normal
Ff	Normal
ff	Cystic fibrosis

A person with the genotype **Ff** is said to be a **carrier** for cystic fibrosis, because they have the cystic fibrosis allele but do not have the condition.

The **Ff** genotype does not cause cystic fibrosis because the **F** allele is **dominant** and the **f** allele is **recessive**. A dominant allele is one that is expressed (has an effect) in a heterozygous organism. A recessive allele is one that is only expressed when a dominant allele is not present.

- The dominant allele should always be symbolised by a capital letter, and the recessive allele by a small letter. The same letter should be used for both (not **F** and **c**, for example).
- If you are able to choose the symbols that you use in a genetics question, then choose ones where the capital and small letter are different in shape, to avoid confusion (not **C** and **c**, for example).

Examiner tip

Note that we say that the *allele* for cystic fibrosis is recessive — not cystic fibrosis itself.

Monohybrid inheritance

This is the inheritance of a single gene.

For example, imagine that a man with the genotype **Ff** and a woman with the genotype **FF** have children. In their testes and ovaries, gametes are produced. In the man, half of his sperm will contain the **F** allele and half will contain the **f** allele. All of the woman's eggs will contain the **F** allele.

We can predict the likely genotypes of any children that they have using a **genetic diagram**. Genetic diagrams should always be set out like this:

Parents' genotypes   Ff   FF

Gametes' genotypes   (F)   (f)   (F)

Offspring genotypes and phenotypes   eggs

                                          (F)

                              (F) | **FF** normal
sperm
                              (f) | **Ff** normal

We can therefore predict that there is an equal chance of any child born to them having the genotype **FF** or **Ff**. There is no chance they will have a child with cystic fibrosis.

If both parents have the genotype **Ff**:

Parents' genotypes   Ff   Ff

Gametes' genotypes   (F)   (f)   (F)   (f)

Offspring genotypes and phenotypes   eggs

                              (F)   (f)

	F	**f**
F	**FF** normal	**Ff** normal
f	**Ff** normal	**ff** cystic fibrosis

sperm

We can therefore predict that, each time they have a child, there is a 1 in 4 chance that it will have the genotype **ff** and have cystic fibrosis.

Table 5 Examples of some inherited traits

Trait	Organism in which it is found	Phenotype produced by dominant allele	Phenotype produced by recessive allele
Albinism	Many, including humans	Normally pigmented skin and iris	Lack of pigment in skin and iris
Thalassaemia	Humans	Normal haemoglobin in blood	Abnormal haemoglobin, which does not transport oxygen effectively
Height	Garden peas	Tall plants	Short plants
Seed morphology	Garden peas	Smooth seeds	Wrinkled seeds

Examiner tip
There is no need to show two gametes for the **FF** parent, because they only produce one kind.

Examiner tip
A genetic diagram is the whole explanation, from 'parents' genotypes' onwards — not just the grid showing the gametes and offspring.

Examiner tip
It is a good idea to write the phenotype as well as the genotype inside the grid (Punnett square).

Knowledge check 25
Draw a genetic diagram to explain the predicted ratios of offspring phenotypes if two pea plants, heterozygous for seed morphology, are bred together.

Gene therapy

Gene therapy is the treatment of a genetic disease by changing the genes in a person's cells. Although attempts have been made to treat several different diseases using gene therapy, there are still many problems to be solved before treatments become widely available and successful.

Gene therapy for cystic fibrosis

For example, attempts have been made to treat cystic fibrosis by introducing the normal CFTR gene into a person's cells. Two methods have been trialled:

- inserting the normal gene into a harmless virus and then allowing the virus to infect cells in the person's respiratory passages — the virus enters the cells and introduces the gene to them
- inserting the gene into little balls of lipid and protein, called liposomes, and spraying these as an aerosol into a person's respiratory passages

The virus and the liposomes are said to be **vectors** — they transfer the gene into the person's cells.

In each case, there was some success in that some of the cells lining the respiratory passages did take up the gene. Because the normal gene is dominant, there only needed to be one copy in a cell for it to produce normal mucus. There is no need to remove the faulty allele first, because it is recessive.

Problems with gene therapy

There were problems with the trials of gene therapy for cystic fibrosis, including:

- Only a few cells took up the normal gene, so only these cells produced normal mucus.
- It was only possible for cells in the respiratory passages to take up the normal gene, not cells in the pancreas or reproductive organs.
- Cells in the surfaces of the respiratory passages do not live for very long, so treatment would need to be repeated every few weeks.
- When using the virus as a vector, some people developed serious lung infections.

Gene therapy has also been used to treat a condition called SCID, in which a child does not have a gene that codes for the production of an enzyme called ADA (adenine deaminase). The condition results in an ineffective immune system. Treatment involves removing some of the child's white blood cells and using a virus to insert a copy of the normal allele of the ADA gene into them. The cells are then replaced in the child's body. This has worked well in terms of causing the cells to produce ADA. However, in some cases the insertion of the gene into the cell's DNA has affected the behaviour of other genes nearby, causing the cells to divide uncontrollably and cause a type of cancer called leukaemia.

Somatic and germ line therapy

Somatic gene therapy involves the modification of genes in a body cell. This affects only the person in whom the treatment has taken place.

Germ line therapy would involve the modification of genes in cells that will produce gametes. This would affect the genes in the gametes, and therefore in an offspring produced from those gametes.

Genetic screening

We have seen that two people with no symptoms of cystic fibrosis can have a child with cystic fibrosis. Many people with cystic fibrosis in their family would like to be able to avoid having a child with the disease, by finding out which alleles they or their unborn child have. Finding out the genes that a person has is called **genetic screening**.

Genetic screening can be used:

- to identify people who are carriers, that is, have a copy of a harmful recessive allele
- in preimplantation genetic diagnosis, that is, checking the genes of an embryo produced *in vitro* (by fertilisation outside the body — 'test tube baby') before it is placed in the mother's uterus
- for prenatal testing, that is, checking the genes of an embryo or fetus in the uterus

A sample of cells is taken from the person to be tested, and the relevant parts of the DNA are analysed to find out whether the allele in question is present. For prenatal testing of a fetus, cells may be taken either by **amniocentesis** or **chorionic villus sampling**.

Amniocentesis can be carried out between 15 and 16 weeks of pregnancy. Chorionic villus sampling can be carried out between 10 and 13 weeks of pregnancy. The needles are inserted using an ultrasound scan for guidance. Both procedures carry a small risk of causing a miscarriage.

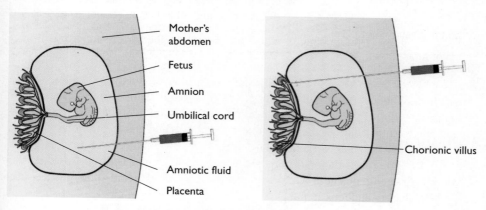

Mother's abdomen

Fetus

Amnion

Umbilical cord

Amniotic fluid

Placenta

Chorionic villus

Figure 37 Amniocentesis and chorionic villus sampling

Implications of prenatal genetic screening

Once potential parents have information about the genes of a potential offspring, they have to make a decision. These decisions have social and ethical implications. For example:

- A choice can be made of which embryos produced *in vitro* are to be implanted into the mother. Most people would agree that it is ethically acceptable to decide not to implant an embryo that has potentially harmful alleles. The law also allows an embryo to be chosen for implantation that has a tissue type that would allow the child to provide a transplant for a sick elder brother or sister, but some people question the ethics of this. The possibility could also arise in the future of choosing an embryo that would grow up to have blond hair or be especially intelligent, which many people would consider not to be good for society and to be unethical.
- If a fetus is found to have alleles for a genetic disease such as cystic fibrosis, the parents have to decide whether the pregnancy should be terminated or not. This raises ethical issues about the right to life of an unborn child, and whether it is desirable that parents determine whether or not a disability would allow a child to have good quality of life.

Opinions differ, and there are no universally accepted 'right' answers. You should be able to appreciate a range of ethical viewpoints, even if you have strong opinions of your own. You can find the latest regulations relating to these issues in the UK, and also recent press releases and discussions, at the web site of the Human Fertilisation and Embryology Authority (**www.hfea.gov.uk**).

Summary

After studying this topic, you should be able to:
- describe semi-conservative replication of DNA
- explain how Meselson and Stahl's experiment provided evidence for semi-conservative replication of DNA
- describe how a gene codes for a sequence of amino acids in a polypeptide
- outline how transcription and translation take place
- describe what is meant by a gene mutation, with reference to cystic fibrosis
- use genetic diagrams to explain examples of monohybrid inheritance
- describe what is meant by gene therapy
- explain the various uses of genetic screening, and discuss social and ethical issues relating to genetic screening

Questions & Answers

In this section there are two sample examination papers, similar to the Edexcel Unit Test papers. All of the questions are based on the topic areas described in the previous sections of the book.

You have 1 hour 15 minutes to do each paper. There are 80 marks on the paper, so you can spend almost 1 minute per mark. If you find you are spending too long on one question, move on to another that you can answer more quickly. If you have time at the end, come back to the difficult one.

Some of the questions require you to recall information that you have learned. Be guided by the number of marks awarded to suggest how much detail you should give in your answer. The more marks there are, the more information you need to give.

Some of the questions require you to use your knowledge and understanding in new situations. Don't be surprised to find something completely new in a question — something you have not seen before. Just think carefully about it, and find something that you do know that will help you to answer it.

Do think carefully before you begin to write. The best answers are short and relevant — if you target your answer well, you can get many marks for a small amount of writing. Don't ramble on and say the same thing several times over, or wander off into answers that have nothing to do with the question. As a general rule, there will be twice as many answer lines as marks. So you should try to answer a 3-mark question in no more than 6 lines of writing. If you are writing much more than that, you almost certainly haven't focused your answer tightly enough.

Look carefully at exactly what each question wants you to do. For example, if it asks you to 'Explain', then you need to say how or why something happens, not just what happens. Many students lose large numbers of marks by not reading the question carefully.

Examiner's comments

Each question is followed by a brief analysis of what to watch out for when answering the question (shown by the icon ⓔ). All student responses are then followed by examiner's comments. These are preceded by the icon ⓔ and indicate where credit is due. In the weaker answers, they also point out areas for improvement, specific problems, and common errors such as lack of clarity, weak or non-existent development, irrelevance, misinterpretation of the question and mistaken meanings of terms.

Sample Paper 1

Question 1

The diagrams below show five molecules found in living organisms.

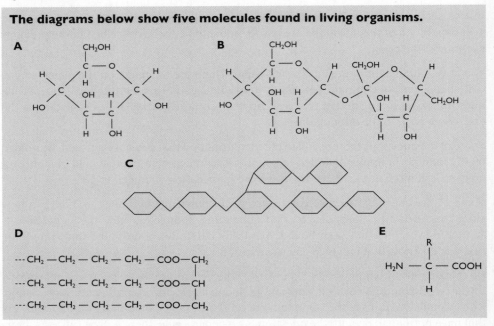

(a) Give the letter of one molecule that fits each of these descriptions.
  (i) the form in which carbohydrates are transported through phloem tissue in plants (1 mark)
  (ii) the form in which carbohydrates are stored in animals (1 mark)
  (iii) a molecule that is insoluble in water (1 mark)
  (iv) a molecule that links together with others to form a polypeptide (1 mark)
  (v) a molecule that contains ester bonds (1 mark)

(b) Explain how the structure of water molecules makes water a good solvent. (3 marks)

Total: 8 marks

ⓔ This question tests your ability to recall structures and functions of biological molecules. Note you should only give *one* letter for each answer in (a).

Student A

(a) (i) A ✗

ⓔ A is a glucose molecule, but plants transport sucrose. Even if you did not know what a sucrose molecule looks like, you should know that it is a disaccharide.

  (ii) C ✓

ⓔ Correct. **1/1**

> **(iii)** E ✗

ⓔ Amino acids are soluble. Either C or D would be correct. **0/1**

> **(iv)** E ✓

ⓔ Correct. **1/1**

> **(v)** D ✓

ⓔ Correct. **1/1**

> **(b)** Water has dipoles and hydrogen bonds, ✓ which help it to dissolve other substances.

ⓔ There are no wrong statements in this answer, but it does not really give an explanation of why water is a good solvent — it just states two facts about water molecules. **1/3**

Student B

> **(a) (i)** B ✓

ⓔ Correct. **1/1**

> **(ii)** C ✓

ⓔ Correct. **1/1**

> **(iii)** D or C ✓

ⓔ Correct. However, student B took an unnecessary risk with (iii), by giving two answers. If the second one had been wrong, it could have negated the first correct one. If you are asked for one answer, it is best to give only one. **1/1**

> **(iv)** E ✓

ⓔ Correct. **1/1**

> **(v)** D ✓

ⓔ Correct. **1/1**

> **(a)** In a water molecule, the hydrogen atoms have a tiny positive electrical charge and the oxygen atom has a similar negative charge. ✓ Other atoms or ions with electrical charges ✓ are attracted ✓ to these charges on the water molecules. This makes them spread about ✓ among the water molecules.

ⓔ This is a good answer — it explains how a substance dissolves in water and relates this clearly to the structure of a water molecule. Student B has earned all four possible marking points, but there is only a maximum of 3 marks available in total. **3/3**

Question 2

A study was carried out between September 2000 and May 2001 into the incidence of coronary heart disease (CHD) in people living in south London. CHD is caused by damage to the coronary arteries, generally involving atherosclerosis.

Doctors in 63 medical practices entered data about their patients into a computer system. Only patients aged 44 years or over were included in the study. In total, information about 100 000 patients was entered into the database. Of these, 6800 patients had CHD.

The table below lists the percentage of these patients with CHD for whom particular risk factors were recorded (rows in bold text in the table) and the percentage who had these risk factors.

	Percentage of CHD patients	
	Women	Men
Blood pressure recorded in previous 5 years	**90**	**89**
Blood pressure above normal	27	26
BMI recorded in previous 2 years	**44**	**51**
Blood cholesterol level above $6\,\text{mmol}\,\text{dm}^{-3}$	59	44
BMI recorded in previous 2 years	**34**	**34**
BMI above $30\,\text{kg}\,\text{m}^{-2}$	29	26
Current smoker	21	25
Prescribed statins	38	49
Prescribed aspirin	59	65

(a) State and explain two reasons why the results of this study do *not* allow us to draw any reliable conclusions about the relationship of these risk factors to the incidence of CHD.   (4 marks)

(b) A further study showed that the death rate from CHD among people who smoked between 15 and 24 cigarettes per day was nine times greater than among people who did not smoke.
Does this prove a causative relationship between smoking and CHD? Explain your answer.   (2 marks)

(c) Explain why patients with CHD may be prescribed the following drugs.
   (i) statins   (2 marks)
   (ii) aspirin   (2 marks)

(d) A person who has a heart attack caused by a blood clot in a coronary artery may be prescribed a drug called heparin. Heparin binds with the enzyme thrombin and stops thrombin binding with its substrate.
   (i)   Name the normal substrate for thrombin.

(1 mark)

   (ii) Suggest how heparin may reduce the risk of any more blood clots forming in the patient's blood vessels.

(3 marks)

Total: 14 marks

ⓔ Parts (a) and (b) of this question are about analysing data, and also test your understanding of correlation and causation. It is important to take time to read all the information very thoroughly before beginning to construct your answer. Note that in (c) you are asked to *explain* — that is, to say how or why. In (d), you are asked to suggest, indicating that you are being asked to work something out using your own knowledge plus the information provided in the question.

Student A

(a) 1 There weren't enough people included in the study. ✗
2 Only people over 44 were included in the study. ✓

ⓔ The first answer is not correct, as there was a very large number in the study (100000 altogether and 6800 with CHD).

The second answer is better — although it is fair enough for a study to look at CHD risks within a particular age range, as this one does. Neither answer develops the point sufficiently to get a second mark. **1/4**

(b) No. It does show that smoking and CHD are correlated. ✓

ⓔ The answer 'no' is correct, but there is not usually a mark for an answer where there are only two possibilities. Here, both marks are for the explanation. This answer makes a good start, but needs to say more to get the second mark. **1/2**

(c) (i) To stop them having more heart attacks ✗
(ii) To stop their blood clotting ✓

ⓔ Once again, student A has managed not to say anything wrong, but has not given enough clear information to get many marks. (i) He/she needs to explain what statins do, and how this helps to stop the person having more heart attacks. Student A has 'described' and not 'explained'. **0/2** (ii) This is a bit better, as we are told what aspirin does in the body, but this is not linked to CHD so only gets 1 mark. **1/2**

(d) (i) Fibrinogen ✓
(ii) It stops fibrinogen turning into fibrin. ✓

ⓔ The answer 'fibrinogen' is correct. **1/1** The answer to (ii) is also correct, but some link needs to be made between fibrin and blood clots, which is what the question asks about. **1/3**

Student B

(a) 1 The researchers didn't collect information about people who did not have CHD, ✓ so we cannot compare ✓ the data for people with it with people without it. 2 Lots of people in the study did not have factors such as their blood pressure recorded. ✓

ⓔ The first answer is good, and it is explained sufficiently to get the second mark. The second answer also starts well, but it doesn't go on to explain how this affects the interpretation of the results of the study. **3/4**

(b) No, though it does strongly suggest that there is some kind of link between them. These data would support a hypothesis that smoking causes CHD, but that's not the same as proving it. ✓ It is possible that something else makes people both smoke and have CHD. ✓

ⓔ This is a really good answer. **2/2**

(c) (i) To lower their blood cholesterol level. ✓
(ii) This reduces the chance of blood clotting ✓ when it shouldn't, which reduces the risk of arteries getting blocked and stopping blood getting to the heart or the brain. ✓

ⓔ The answer to (i) is correct, but needs to explain how reducing blood cholesterol level could reduce the risk of CHD in order to get the second mark. **1/2**

The answer to (ii) is good and gets both marks. **2/2**

(d) (i) ~~Fibrin Fibrinogen~~ Fibrin (fibrinogen)
(ii) When blood clots, the soluble protein fibrin is converted to the insoluble protein fibrin, which forms fibres ✓ across the wound in which platelets and red blood cells get trapped to form the clot. Thrombin changes it into fibrin, so if heparin stops it doing it then it won't clot.

ⓔ Student B needed to spend a bit more time checking this answer, as marks have been lost because of poor communication. He/she was obviously not sure of the answer to (i), but should have made it clear which answer was intended. The examiner cannot be sure whether he/she means fibrin or fibrinogen, so cannot give a mark. **0/1**

In (ii), student B starts well, but unfortunately writes 'fibrin' twice — the first one should be fibrinogen. The last sentence is full of 'it's and the examiner cannot be sure what each 'it' refers to. It is a good idea to avoid 'it' where you can. Here, the student probably meant that thrombin changes fibrinogen into fibrin, so if heparin stops thrombin doing this, then the blood will not clot. **1/3**

Question 3

The diagram below shows a small part of a human lung as it appears through a microscope.

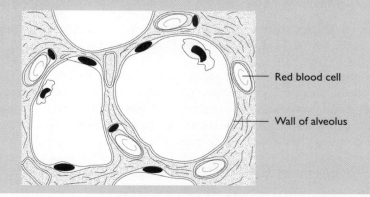

Red blood cell

Wall of alveolus

(a) Name the type of blood vessel in which the red blood cell is present.   (1 mark)

(b) Describe and explain two ways in which the structure of the alveoli, shown in the diagram, enables gas exchange to take place rapidly.   (4 marks)

(c) Suggest why large organisms such as mammals need specialised gas exchange surfaces, whereas small organisms such as a single-celled *Amoeba* do not.   (2 marks)

(d) Cystic fibrosis is a genetic disease in which the mucus in the alveoli is much thicker than normal.
    (i) Explain how this impairs the functioning of the gas exchange system.   (3 marks)
    (ii) Outline one other effect of cystic fibrosis on health.   (2 marks)

Total: 12 marks

ⓔ Try to use correct scientific terminology when answering questions such as (d) (i).

Student A

(a) Capillary ✓

ⓔ This is correct. **1/1**

(b) They have a large surface area. ✓
They are thin, so oxygen can diffuse across quickly. ✓

ⓔ The statement about a large surface area is correct, but the answer also needs to say why this enables gas exchange to take place rapidly (because the question asks you to 'explain'). The second answer is not sufficiently clear — what is thin? It is not the whole alveoli that are thin, but their walls. The second part of this answer does give a clear explanation of why this helps gas exchange to take place quickly. **2/4**

(c) Large organisms have small surface areas compared to their volume, ✓ so they need extra surface ✓ to be able to get enough oxygen.

ⓔ There is a correct and clear statement about surface area to volume ratio, and the answer also just gets a second mark. However, this isn't clear — see student B for a better explanation. **2/2**

(d) (i) The mucus clogs up the lungs, so oxygen can't get into the blood. You get infections ✓ like bronchitis and have to cough a lot.

ⓔ 'Clogs up' is not a good scientific term, and examiners in general don't like you to use this type of language in an exam answer. Try to choose words carefully — for example, here you could say that 'The sticky mucus forms a thick layer lining the alveoli, making it more difficult for oxygen to diffuse from the alveoli into the blood.' The statement about infections is correct, but perhaps the candidate could also say *why* the mucus gets infected. **1/3**

(ii) It makes it difficult to digest your food ✓ and makes people sterile.

ⓔ Student A has given two effects, not one. He gets 1 mark for the statement about digestive problems, but needs to expand on this point rather than starting to describe a second effect. **1/2**

Student B

(a) Capillary ✓

ⓔ Correct. **1/1**

(b) Large surface area ✓ — so more oxygen and carbon dioxide molecules can diffuse across at the same time ✓.
Good supply of oxygen — to maintain a diffusion gradient between the alveoli and the blood.

ⓔ The first way is correct and well explained. However, the second, although true, does not answer the question which is about the *structure* of the alveoli. **2/4**.

(c) They have small surface area to volume ratios, ✓ but an *Amoeba* has a large surface area to volume ratio. The oxygen that diffuses in across the surface has to supply the whole volume ✓ of the animal, so in a large animal that is not enough and they have specialised gas exchange surfaces to increase the surface area ✓ and let more oxygen diffuse in.

ⓔ This is a good answer. All the important points are there and it is clearly expressed. **2/2**

(d) **(i)** The mucus in the lungs is much stickier and thicker than usual, ✓ so it gets stuck in the lungs ✓ and so bacteria can get into it and breed and cause infections. ✓ It makes the gas exchange surface thicker, so it takes longer ✓ for oxygen to diffuse through it into the blood.

ⓔ Again, this is very well explained. Four ticks, so a maximum of the three possible marks. **3/3**

(ii) Mucus blocks the pancreatic duct, ✓ so pancreatic juice can't get into the small intestine and digest ✓ the food.

ⓔ Good — a clear description with enough detail for the second mark. **2/2**

Question 4

The diagram below shows a small part of a DNA molecule during replication.

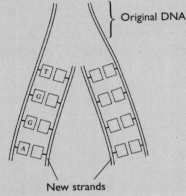

Original DNA

New strands

(a) (i) Name the part of a cell in which DNA replication takes place.　　(1 mark)
(ii) Complete the diagram by writing the letters of the correct bases in each of the empty squares.　　(2 marks)
(iii) Explain why this is known as semi-conservative replication.　　(2 marks)

(b) Meselson and Stahl carried out an experiment to determine whether DNA replication is conservative or semi-conservative. They grew bacteria for many generations in a medium containing heavy nitrogen (^{15}N) and then transferred them to a medium containing normal nitrogen (^{14}N).
DNA was extracted from the bacteria when they had been growing in the medium containing ^{15}N, and then when they had been growing for one and two generations in the medium containing ^{14}N.
The DNA samples were centrifuged in a calcium chloride solution. The diagram below shows some of the results.

Sample 1
Bacteria grown in medium containing ^{15}N

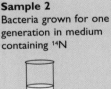

Sample 2
Bacteria grown for one generation in medium containing ^{14}N

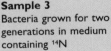

Sample 3
Bacteria grown for two generations in medium containing ^{14}N

(i) **Explain how the results for Sample 1 and Sample 2 support the hypothesis that DNA replication is semi-conservative and not conservative.**
(2 marks)

(ii) **Complete the diagram by drawing the results you would expect in the tube for Sample 3.**
(1 mark)

(c) **Explain why it is important that the new DNA molecules formed during replication are exactly the same as the original molecule.**
(5 marks)

Total: 13 marks

ⓔ There is a lot of reading in this question. You should already be familiar with Meselson and Stahl's experiment, but you should still take time to read all the information carefully, as you will need it when answering the questions.

(a) (i) Nucleus

ⓔ Correct. **1/1**

(ii)

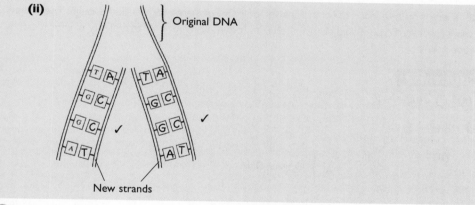

Original DNA

New strands

ⓔ All correct. **2/2**

(iii) Because it keeps one strand of DNA

ⓔ This answer is not clear enough to be awarded any marks. It is not clear what 'it' means — the candidate is probably referring to the new DNA molecule but does not say so. **0/2**

(b) (i) Because there is only one kind of DNA ✓ — there would be two sorts if it was conservative.

ⓔ Student A is thinking along the right lines and what he/she says is correct. However, for the second mark, he/she needs to say what the two kinds of DNA would be, or where they would appear in the tube, if the replication was conservative. **1/2**

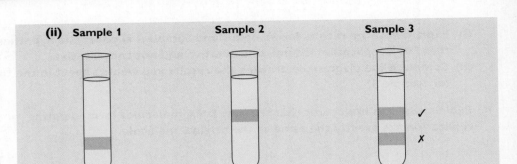

(ii) Sample 1   Sample 2   Sample 3

ℯ You would expect to see two bands, one level with the band in sample 2 and one above the level of sample 2 , so only one of these is correct. The lower band is wrong — you would not get any all heavy DNA because the cell is using ^{14}N to make its new DNA. So some of its new DNA will contain all ^{14}N, and some will contain half ^{14}N and half ^{15}N. **1/2**

(c) The DNA tells a cell what to do. It tells it what proteins to make. ✓ If a cell doesn't get a complete set of correct DNA, it will not make the right proteins so it might die.

ℯ There is nothing incorrect in this answer, but it is nowhere near detailed enough. There are 5 marks allocated (you would be given ten lines to write on) implying that plenty of information is needed. **1/5**

Student B

(a) (i) Nucleus ✓

ℯ Correct. **1/1**

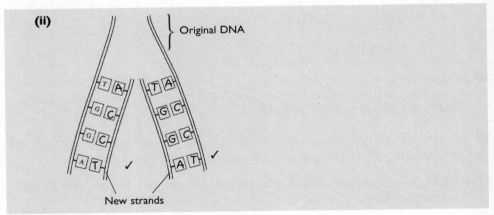

(ii)   Original DNA

New strands

ℯ Correct. **2/2**

(iii) The new molecule of DNA that is made contains one strand from the original molecule ✓ and one newly made strand. ✓

ⓔ Very clear and completely correct. **2/2**

(b) (i) If it was conservative, then the new DNA molecules would contain all ^{14}N, so they would be light and would make a separate band higher up the tube. ✓ The old DNA molecules would still contain all ^{15}N, so they would make a band low down in the tube, ✓ like sample 1. Having just one band for all the DNA means all the molecules must be the same, ✓ with one strand in each molecule containing ^{14}N and the other strand containing ^{15}N. ✓

ⓔ An excellent answer — though it would take up a lot more than the four lines allocated. Student B has described clearly what you would see if the type of replication was conservative (and why) and then done the same for what you would see if it was semi-conservative. Four ticks, a maximum of 2 marks available. **2/2**

(ii)

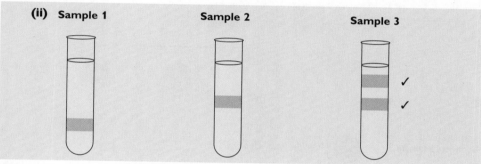

ⓔ Correct. **2/2**

(c) The sequence of bases in a DNA molecule codes for the sequence of amino acids in a protein molecule. ✓ Three bases code for one amino acid. ✓ If a cell does not have a complete set of DNA, or if the DNA is different, then it will not use the correct amino acids when proteins are being made. ✓ So the protein won't have the same primary structure ✓ and therefore won't have the same shape. ✓ So the protein won't work properly. ✓

ⓔ Again, an excellent answer. Student B has worked logically through the process by which DNA affects a cell's behaviour and given a very concise and entirely correct explanation. **5/5**

Question 5

Albinism is a condition in which the pigment melanin is not formed in skin or other parts of the body. Albinism is caused by a recessive allele of the gene that codes for a protein involved in the formation of melanin.

(a) Explain what is meant by each of the following terms:

    (i) allele   (1 mark)

    (ii) recessive   (1 mark)

(b) The pedigree diagram shows the incidence of albinism in three generations of a family.

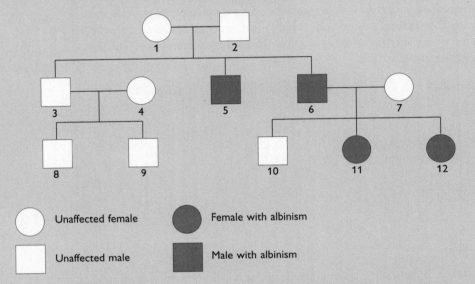

    ⬜ Unaffected female   ⬛ Female with albinism

    ⬜ Unaffected male   ⬛ Male with albinism

    (i) Construct a complete genetic diagram to show how person 5 inherited albinism from his parents.
In your genetic diagram, use the letters A to represent the normal allele and a to represent the allele for albinism.   (4 marks)

    (ii) Alleles such as the one that codes for albinism initially arise by mutation. Explain how the pedigree diagram indicates that the mutation for albinism did not initially arise in person 5.   (2 marks)

    (iii) What are the chances that person 10 is heterozygous for albinism?   (1 mark)

    (iv) If persons 6 and 7 had a fourth child, what are the chances that it would have albinism?   (1 mark)

Total: 10 marks

ℯ It is a good idea to learn definitions of terms, such as those in (a). In (b), remember that a genetic diagram includes much more than just a Punnett square.

Student A

(a) (i) A form of a gene ✓

ⓔ Correct. **1/1**

(ii) The opposite of dominant — it is not as strong as a dominant gene.

ⓔ A poor answer — the term 'strong' is not a good one to use in this context. **0/1**

(b) (i)   **Aa** ✓

	AA	**Aa**
Aa	**Aa**	**aa** ✓

ⓔ This is not a complete genetic diagram. Student A has worked out the correct genotypes of the parents, and gets a mark for that. However, he/she has not shown the genotypes of the gametes they would produce. He/she correctly shows the genotypes of the possible offspring, but does not show which of these has albinism. **2/4**

(ii) The allele **a** is recessive, so you would need two of them to make you albino. ✓ If only one allele had mutated, ✓ you would not be albino.

ⓔ This is correct. **2/2**

(iii) 50:50

ⓔ Correct. (Student A could also have said 1:1 or 1 in 2 or 50%, which all mean the same thing.) **1/1**

(iv) There's no chance, ✗ because they already have two children with albinism and the chance of getting albinism is only 50:50.

ⓔ This is not correct. It is true that the chance of children born to the couple getting albinism is 50:50, but this applies to each child. Every time a new child is conceived, there is a 50:50 chance it will get an **a** allele from each parent, no matter what the genotypes of any older children.

Student B

(a) A particular form of a gene ✓

ⓔ Correct. **1/1**

(b) (i)

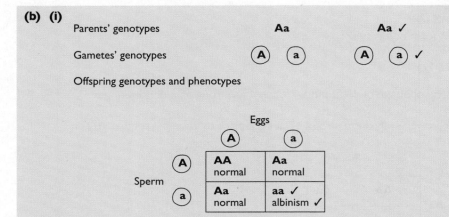

Parents' genotypes   Aa   Aa ✓

Gametes' genotypes   (A) (a)   (A) (a) ✓

Offspring genotypes and phenotypes

We can therefore predict that, each time they have a child, there is a 1 in 4 chance that it will have the genotype **aa** and have albinism.

ⓔ This is an entirely correct and complete genetic diagram. Student B has clearly shown (and labelled) the parents' genotypes, the genotypes of the gametes, the possible genotypes of the offspring and their phenotypes. **4/4**

(ii) If the mutation happened in a body cell, then only that cell would be affected, not their whole body. ✓ If the mutation was in a gamete, then it would affect the whole body of the child that grew after fertilisation ✓ — but you would need two mutations like that because the allele for albinism is recessive. ✓ So it must have happened in both of the parents when their gametes were being made, or maybe much further back in the generations than that.

ⓔ This is a correct answer. **2/2**

(iii) 1 in 2 ✓

ⓔ Correct. **1/1**

(iv) 1 in 2 ✓

ⓔ Correct. **1/1**

Question 6

The diagram below shows pressure changes in the left atrium and left ventricle of the heart and the aorta during the cardiac cycle.

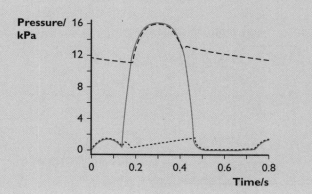

(a) Calculate how many heart beats there will be in 1 minute.   (2 marks)

(b) (i) On the diagram, indicate the point at which the semilunar valves in the aorta snap shut.   (1 mark)
   (ii) Explain what causes the semilunar valves to shut at this point in the cardiac cycle.   (2 marks)
   (iii) On the diagram, indicate the period when the left ventricle is contracting.   (1 mark)
   (iv) On the diagram, draw a line to show the changes in pressure in the right ventricle.   (2 marks)

(c) After the blood leaves the heart, it passes into the arteries. The blood pressure gradually reduces and becomes more steady as the blood passes through the arteries.
Explain what causes this reduction and steadying of the blood pressure.   (2 marks)

Total: 10 marks

ⓔ Most of this question is about being able to interpret a graph precisely. Take care to be as accurate as possible with your answers to (b) (i), (iii) and (iv).

Student A

(a) 1 cycle in 0.8 seconds ✓ so in 60 seconds there will be 60 × 0.8 ✗ = 48 beats

ⓔ The student has read the length of one cycle correctly, but the calculation is wrong. **1/2**

(b) (i)

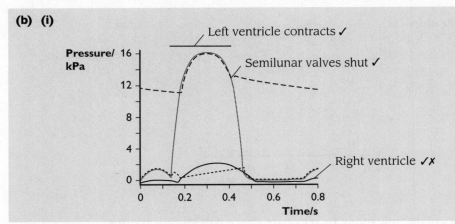

ⓔ Correct. **1/1**

(ii) The valves shut when the ventricle starts to relax. ✓

ⓔ This answer is correct as far as it goes, but student A needs to give more information in order to get the second mark. **1/2**

(iii) See diagram

ⓔ Correct. **1/1**

(iv) See diagram

ⓔ This answer is partly correct. The pressure in the right ventricle is correctly shown as less than that in the left ventricle, but it should be contracting and relaxing at exactly the same times as the left ventricle. **1/2**

(c) The pressure gets less as the blood gets further away from the heart. ✓ The muscle in the walls of the arteries contracts ✗ and relaxes to push the blood along, and it does this in between heart beats so the pulse gets evened out.

ⓔ The first statement is correct. However, it is not correct that the muscles in the artery wall contract and relax. **1/2**

Student B

(a) 60/0.8 ✓ = 75 beats per minute ✓

ⓔ Correct. **2/2**

(b) (i)

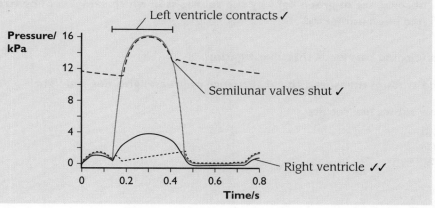

ⓔ Correct. **1/1**

   (ii) They close when the pressure of the blood inside the arteries is higher than inside the ventricles ✓ — the blood therefore pushes down on the valves and makes them shut. ✓

ⓔ Correct. **2/2**

   (iii) See diagram.

ⓔ Correct. **1/1**

   (iv) See diagram.

ⓔ Correct. **2/2**

(c) As the blood is forced into the artery as the ventricle contracts, ✓ it pushes outwards on the artery wall, making the elastic tissue stretch. ✓ In between heart beats, the pressure of the blood inside the artery falls, and the elastic tissue recoils. ✓ So the wall keeps expanding and springing back. When it springs back it pushes on the blood in between ✓ heart beats, so this levels up the pressure changes.

ⓔ This answer explains very well why the blood pressure levels out. However, it does not mention the overall fall in blood pressure. All the same, this is an excellent answer which gets full marks. **2/2**

Question 7

A student carried out an investigation into the effect of temperature on the permeability of the cell surface membrane of beetroot cells. She decided to measure permeability by using a colorimeter to measure the absorbance of green light by the solutions in which samples of beetroot had been immersed.

(a) Describe how she could carry out this investigation. (5 marks)

(b) Suggest why the student measured the absorbance of green light, not red light. (1 mark)

(c) The graph below shows her results.

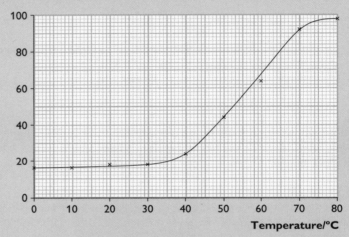

(i) With reference to the graph, describe the effect of temperature on the absorbance of light in the colorimeter. (3 marks)

(ii) With reference to the structure of cell membranes, explain the effects you have described in (i). (4 marks)

Total: 13 marks

ⓔ Part (a) requires a description of experimental procedure. Make sure your answer is quite detailed — mention numbers, temperatures and times.

When describing what is shown by a graph, outline the general trend, then home in on places where the gradient changes. Quote particular coordinates.

Student A

(a) She should cut up some pieces of beetroot, all the same size. ✓ Put them into water at different temperatures ✓ and leave them for the same time. ✓ Take the beetroot pieces out. Put the water in a colorimeter tube and measure how much light goes through it. ✓ The less light goes through, the more the membrane has leaked. ✓

ⓔ This answer just gets 5 marks, though there is a lot of detail missing. **5/5**

(b) Because this gives more accurate results.

ⓔ This answer does not provide any specific information relating to this experiment. **0/1**

(c) (i) Between 0 and 30 the absorbance goes up very slightly. ✓ Above 40°C it goes up very quickly. ✗ Then it starts to level out at about 70°C. ✓

ⓔ Student A has correctly identified the three main regions of the graph, stating where changes in gradient occur. However, the term 'quickly' is not correct because the graph does not show anything about time. He/she could also have gained a third mark by quoting some figures from the graph. **2/3**

(ii) High temperatures damage the proteins in the membrane. ✓ They get denatured, so they leave holes ✓ in the membrane that the beetroot pigment can get through.

ⓔ This is a good answer as far as it goes; clearly expressed. **2/4**

Student B

(a) Cut lots of pieces of beetroot, all exactly the same size ✓ and all from the same beetroot. ✓ Wash the beetroot pieces. ✓ Immerse them in the same volume ✓ of water. Put the tubes in water baths at different temperatures, ranging from 0 to 90°C. ✓ After 10 minutes, ✓ take the beetroot pieces out of the tubes. Put the water into a colorimeter using a green filter and measure the absorbance of each lot of water. The greater the absorbance, the more red pigment had escaped so the more permeable ✓ the membrane.

ⓔ An excellent answer. **5/5**

(b) Beetroot pigment is red, so it absorbs all other colours of light and reflects red light. ✓ Using a red filter we would not see any difference between the tubes.

ⓔ Again, a very good answer. **1/1**

(c) (i) The general trend is that the higher the temperature, the greater the absorbance. Between 0 and 30°C, the absorbance increases very slightly ✓ from 16 to 18 arbitrary units. Above 40°C it increases much more steeply, ✓ levelling off at about 75°C. ✓ The maximum absorbance is 98 arbitrary units.

ⓔ A good answer. However, although student B has quoted some figures from the graph, he/she has not manipulated them in any way — for example, he/she could have calculated the increase in absorbance between 0 and 30°C. **3/3**

(ii) As temperature increases, the phospholipids and protein molecules in the membrane move about faster ✓ and with more energy. This leaves gaps in the membrane, so the beetroot pigment molecules can get through ✓ and escape from the cell. The protein molecules start to lose their shape at high temperatures ✓ because their hydrogen bonds break, ✓ so the protein pores get wider ✓ which increases permeability.

ⓔ An excellent answer. **4/4**

Sample Paper 2

Question 1

The diagram shows the fluid mosaic model of membrane structure.

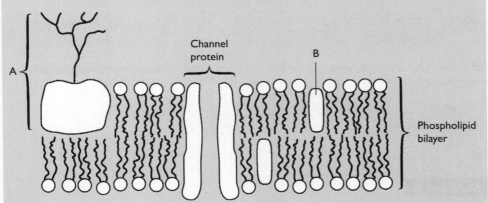

(a) **Name the molecules A and B.**   (2 marks)

(b) **Explain how the properties of phospholipids cause them to form a bilayer.**   (3 marks)

(c) **Explain why the representation of membrane structure is said to be a 'model'.**   (2 marks)

(d) **Sodium ions can pass across cell membranes by facilitated diffusion or by active transport.**
   (i) **Explain why it is not possible for sodium ions to diffuse freely through the phospholipid bilayer.**   (2 marks)
   (ii) **With reference to the diagram of the membrane above, explain how sodium ions could move across the membrane by facilitated diffusion.**   (2 marks)

Total: 11 marks

ⓔ Most parts of this question ask you to 'explain' — so you need to say *how* or *why*.

Student A

(a) A protein, ✓ B cholesterol ✓

ⓔ Both correct. **2/2**

(b) They have hydrophobic heads which go towards water and hydrophilic tails that go away from it. ✓

ⓔ Student A has muddled the terms 'hydrophobic' and 'hydrophilic'. However, he/she has correctly stated that the heads and tails 'go' towards and away from water respectively, which is not well expressed but is just enough to get 1 mark. **1/3**

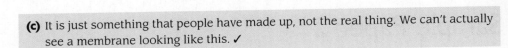

(c) It is just something that people have made up, not the real thing. We can't actually see a membrane looking like this. ✓

ⓔ This is true, but student A fails to explain that the structure of the membrane has not just been 'made up', but had been deduced from experimental evidence about how membranes behave. **1/2**

(d) (i) They have a charge ✓ on them, so they can't go through the phospholipids which are hydrophobic.

ⓔ Student A has the right idea, but needs to make clear that it is the phospholipid tails that are hydrophobic. **1/2**

(ii) They could go through the protein channel, ✓ down their concentration gradient. ✓

ⓔ Concise and entirely correct. **2/2**

Student B

(a) A protein, ✓ B cholesterol ✓

ⓔ Both correct. **2/2**

(b) Their hydrophilic heads are attracted to water, ✓ and their hydrophobic tails try to get away from it, ✓ which they can do by putting their tails together and their heads facing outwards. ✓

ⓔ A clear and correct answer. **3/3**

(c) The structure of the membrane has been worked out because we know a lot about the properties of membranes and this model can explain all of those properties. ✓ So even though we can't see ✓ all the molecules in a membrane, we are fairly sure this is what it would be like.

ⓔ A good answer. **2/2**

(d) (i) Sodium ions are only small, but they have a positive charge, ✓ so they are repelled from the hydrophobic tails ✓ of the phospholipids and can't get through.

ⓔ Correct. **2/2**

(ii) They can diffuse through the protein channels. ✓

ⓔ This is correct, but the answer does not explain what 'diffuse' means so has only given half of the required explanation. **1/2**

Question 2

(a) **The diagrams below show a short length of DNA in the gene that codes for the CFTR protein. The top diagram shows the normal DNA, and the bottom diagram shows the DNA from a person with cystic fibrosis.**

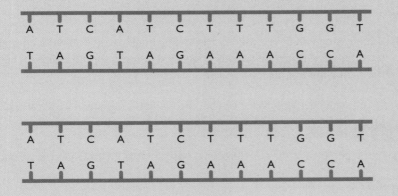

   (i) **Describe the difference between the DNA in the person with cystic fibrosis, compared with the normal DNA.** (2 marks)

   (ii) **Explain fully how this difference results in the production of non-functioning CFTR protein.** (5 marks)

(b) **A woman whose partner comes from a family in which some members have cystic fibrosis becomes pregnant. She and her partner decide that she will have an amniocentesis procedure to find out if the embryo will have cystic fibrosis.**

   (i) **Describe how amniocentesis is carried out.** (3 marks)

   (ii) **Briefly discuss the ethical issues arising from the couple's decision.** (3 marks)

Total: 13 marks

ⓔ Note that (a) (i) asks for differences, so you should refer to both the lengths of DNA. In (b) (ii), the command word 'discuss' means that you should try to mention two different points of view.

Student A

(a) (i) The DNA in the cystic fibrosis person is missing three bases ✓ in the middle.

ⓔ Correct as far as it goes. A better answer would say which three bases are missing. **1/2**

   (ii) There would be an amino acid missed out of the protein that is made. ✓ So the protein would not be the right shape ✓ and it would not carry out its job properly. ✓

ⓔ Again, this is correct as far as it goes, but there are 5 marks available so much more needs to be said. **3/5**

(b) (i) It is done at about 15–16 weeks. ✓ A long needle ✓ is put through the mother's stomach into her uterus and some liquid from inside the amnion ✓ is taken out and tested for DNA. ✓ If they find a wrong gene for cystic fibrosis, then the baby might have it.

ⓔ This is all correct — though the word 'stomach' is not used correctly. The stomach is an organ in the digestive system. **3/3**

(ii) If their baby will have cystic fibrosis, they might want to have the pregnancy terminated. ✓ But it isn't always right that parents should choose whether their baby lives or dies. ✓

ⓔ Two relevant statements are made here, but there is not enough for a third mark. **2/3**

Student B

(a) (i) In the person with cystic fibrosis, a base triplet CTT or GAA ✓ is missing. ✓

ⓔ Correct. **2/2**

(ii) These three bases could have coded for an amino acid, ✓ or it could be part of two other triplets on either side of it. ✓ So an amino acid might be completely missing ✓ in the protein, or there might be some different amino acids. ✓ This would change the primary structure ✓ of the protein that is made, which in turn would change the shape it makes when it folds up into its tertiary structure. ✓ This protein should form a chloride channel in a cell membrane, so if it is the wrong shape the chloride channel won't work ✓ and chloride ions won't go out of the cell.

ⓔ An excellent answer, giving a lot of information very concisely. **5/5**

(b) (i) A long needle is pushed through the mother's abdominal wall ✓ and into the amniotic fluid. A sample of fluid ✓ is taken out and checked to see if contains the cystic fibrosis allele. ✓

ⓔ All correct, though no mention of when the procedure could be carried out. **3/3**

(ii) If parents know their child will be born with a disability, they have to decide whether to keep it or have the pregnancy terminated. ✓ On the one hand, a termination would prevent the child suffering. ✓ On the other hand, the child might be able to live a very worthwhile life even if they have a disability. ✓

ⓔ A good answer that puts two different points of view. **3/3**

Edexcel AS Biology

Question 3

A student carried out an investigation into the effect of substrate concentration on the rate of breakdown of hydrogen peroxide by the enzyme catalase.

He added catalase solution to samples of hydrogen peroxide of different concentrations and measured the volume of oxygen given off. The graph below shows his results.

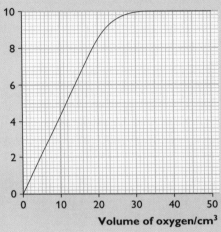

(a) State three variables that the student should keep constant in this investigation.   (3 marks)

(b) Describe the results shown in the graph.   (2 marks)

(c) Explain why it is important to measure the rate of reaction near the start of the reaction, rather than timing how long it takes for the reaction to finish.   (3 marks)

(d) The diagram shows the activation energy required to cause a substrate to change into a product.

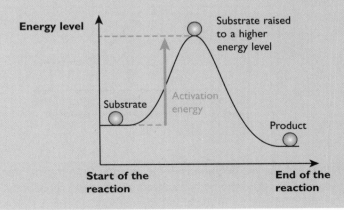

Sketch a similar diagram for the same reaction when catalysed by an enzyme. Label your diagram to show how it differs from the above. (2 marks)

(e) An enzyme in the liver converts lipids to cholesterol. Some of this cholesterol is then transported from the liver as **LDLs**. Statins are drugs which bind with the active site of this enzyme, preventing the normal substrate from binding to it. Use this information, and your own knowledge, to suggest how statins help to reduce the incidence of cardiovascular disease (**CVD**). (6 marks)

Total: 16 marks

ℯ Part (c) is not easy — try writing a list of points you want to make before constructing your final answer. Part (e) has 6 marks, so your answer should be thorough and detailed.

Student A

(a) enzyme concentration, ✓ temperature, ✓ volume

ℯ The first two are correct. The statement 'volume' needs to say what the volume is of — it could be volume of enzyme solution, or volume of hydrogen peroxide solution, or total volume. **2/3**

(b) As the concentration of hydrogen peroxide increases, the volume of oxygen increases ✓ then levels off at about 10% hydrogen peroxide and 30 cm³ of oxygen. ✓

ℯ All correct. **2/2**

(c) Because this is when the reaction is fastest. ✓

ℯ This is true, but needs more for the second and third marks. **1/3**

(d)

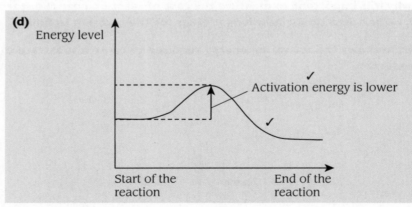

ℯ All correct. **2/2**

(e) If the substrate can't bind with the enzyme, then the enzyme can't make cholesterol. ✓ So the body has less cholesterol in the blood. So there won't be as many plaques ✓ in the blood vessels so less atherosclerosis, ✓ so less heart attacks and strokes. ✓

ⓔ This is again all correct as far as it goes, but more detail is needed for the remaining 2 marks. **4/6**

Student B

(a) The length of time the oxygen is collected for; ✓ the concentration of the enzyme; ✓ the temperature ✓

ⓔ All correct. **3/3**

(b) As the substrate (hydrogen peroxide) increases, the rate of reaction (as measured by the volume of oxygen given off) also increases, ✓ up until the hydrogen peroxide is 10%. Then it levels off.

ⓔ This time, student B has not given quite such a good answer as student A, as he/she has not stated the value for the maximum oxygen volume. **1/2**

(c) The reaction rate is fastest right at the start, ✓ then it starts to slow down as the substrate gets changed into product. ✓ So the substrate concentration varies with time — it doesn't stay constant. ✓ If we measured how long it took for the reaction to finish, we'd actually find it took longer the more substrate there is, ✓ because there would be more of it to break down.

ⓔ A very clear explanation, showing that student B really understands this difficult concept. **3/3**

(d) Energy level

Activation energy is lower ✓ ✓

Start of the reaction   End of the reaction

ⓔ All correct. **2/2**

(e) The substrate will not be changed into cholesterol in the liver. ✓ The liver will make fewer LDLs ✓ to transport the cholesterol round the body. Less cholesterol will get deposited in artery walls, ✓ so less plaques will form. ✓ So the arteries won't get narrow ✓ and there is less chance that a blood clot ✓ will form inside an artery. So it is less likely that blood vessels will get blocked or burst, and so the coronary arteries will be able to go on supplying the heart muscle with nutrients and oxygen ✓ so the heart will be able to go on working properly.

ⓔ An excellent answer. **6/6**

Question 4

The diagram below shows part of a blood clot.

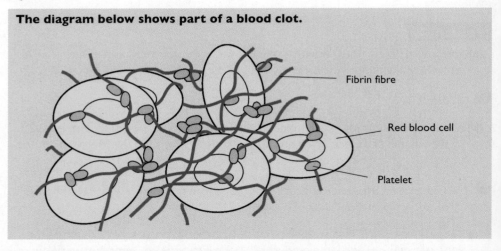

(a) Describe the roles of platelets in the formation of a blood clot. (3 marks)

(b) Fibrin and fibrinogen are proteins. Fibrinogen molecules are changed to fibrin molecules during blood clotting. Suggest how the structure of a fibrin molecule differs from that of a fibrinogen molecule. (2 marks)

(c) The diagram shows two amino acid molecules.

$$H_2N - \underset{\underset{H}{|}}{\overset{\overset{R}{|}}{C}} - COOH \qquad H_2N - \underset{\underset{H}{|}}{\overset{\overset{R}{|}}{C}} - COOH$$

Draw a diagram to show how these amino acids could link together to form a dipeptide molecule. Label and name the bond that links them together. (3 marks)

Total: 8 marks

ℯ This is a straightforward question — as long as you have remembered all of the relevant facts.

Student A

(a) They become sticky ✓ and they release calcium ions. ✓

🄔 Two correct and relevant statements. **2/3**

(b) Fibrin molecules are fibrous, ✓ and fibrinogen is globular. ✓

🄔 Very brief, but just enough to get both marks. **2/2**

(c)

$$H_2N - \underset{\underset{H}{|}}{\overset{\overset{R}{|}}{C}} - COOH \;+\; H_2N - \underset{\underset{H}{|}}{\overset{\overset{R}{|}}{C}} - COOH \longrightarrow \quad H_2N - \underset{\underset{H}{|}}{\overset{\overset{R}{|}}{C}} - CO \overset{\checkmark}{-} HN - \underset{\underset{H}{|}}{\overset{\overset{R}{|}}{C}} - COOH$$

$$+$$

$$H_2O \; \checkmark$$

🄔 Student A correctly shows the formation of a peptide bond and the production of a water molecule but has not done as the question asked and labelled the bond. **2/3**

Student B

(a) When they contact damaged tissue, they are activated. ✓ They release thromboplastin ✓ which makes prothrombin turn into thrombin, ✓ which is what makes fibrinogen turn into fibrin and form fibres. The platelets also release calcium ions ✓ which help that to happen.

🄔 A good answer. **3/3**

(b) Fibrin is globular ✓ and soluble, but fibrinogen is fibrous ✓ and insoluble.

🄔 Simple, but all correct. There was no need to mention solubility, as the question only asked for 'structure'. **2/2**

(c)

Peptide bond ✓

$$H_2N - \underset{\underset{H}{|}}{\overset{\overset{R}{|}}{C}} - COOH \;+\; H_2N - \underset{\underset{H}{|}}{\overset{\overset{R}{|}}{C}} - COOH \longrightarrow \quad H_2N - \underset{\underset{H}{|}}{\overset{\overset{R}{|}}{C}} - CO \overset{\diagup}{\underset{\checkmark}{-}} HN - \underset{\underset{H}{|}}{\overset{\overset{R}{|}}{C}} - COOH$$

🄔 Student B has forgotten to show a water molecule being given off. **2/3**

Question 5

Laboratory-based experiments have frequently indicated that vitamin C may protect against cardiovascular disease by deactivating free radicals, which are known to damage cells. Many people take vitamin C tablets on a regular basis, hoping that this may reduce their risk of developing CVD.

In 2008, the results of a very large trial were published. The trial involved 14 641 men, all aged 50 or over, who were randomly assigned in equal numbers to take either vitamin C or a placebo. The participants did not know which of these they were taking. All major cardiovascular events, such as a heart attack or stroke, were recorded. The study ran between 1997 and 2007.

At the end of the study, 619 men who had been taking vitamin C had suffered a major cardiovascular event, compared with 626 taking the placebo.

(a) What can be concluded from this study regarding the effectiveness of vitamin C supplements in preventing CVD?
(2 marks)

(b) (i) State one feature of this study that helps to make the results reliable. (1 mark)
(ii) State two features of this study that help to make the results valid. (2 marks)

(c) The body mass index of each participant in the study was also measured. The table shows some of the results.

Body mass index	Number of major cardiovascular events	
	Men taking vitamin C	Men taking placebo
25 or below	90	89
25–29	27	26
30 or above	44	51

Explain why these data do not give us any useful information about any link between body mass index and the risk of a major cardiovascular event.
(3 marks)

(d) Describe how a student could measure the concentration of vitamin C in a sample of apple juice.
(6 marks)

Total: 14 marks

ⓔ Although you may feel under time pressure, it is very important to read all the information in the question very carefully — and probably at least twice — before you begin to write any answers.

Student A

(a) Vitamin C helps a little bit, but not much.

ⓔ This answer is not specific enough or clear enough to earn a mark at AS. **0/2**

(b) (i) There were a lot of subjects in the study. ✓

ⓔ A correct answer — the greater the number of samples in a study, the greater the reliability. **1/1**

    (ii) The people who weren't given vitamin C were given a placebo instead, ✓ so we know it wasn't just taking a pill that had an effect. And there were the same numbers of them taking vitamin C and taking the placebo.

ⓔ The first point is correct. No explanation was asked for, so we don't need the second part of that first sentence. The second sentence is a correct description of the study but it is not a good choice — just having equal numbers does not make the results more valid. **1/2**

(c) We don't know how many people in the study were in each of these BMI groups. ✓

ⓔ A correct statement, but it is just a statement and does not explain as the question required. **1/3**

(d) Get some vitamin C of known concentration ✓ and put it into a burette. ✓ Get some DCPIP solution and put it in a conical flask. ✓ Add vitamin C to the DCPIP until the DCPIP goes colourless and record the volume. ✓
Then do the same with the apple juice and compare the results.

ⓔ The basic method is fine — you can do this with either the vitamin C or the DCPIP in the burette. The statement about what to do with the apple juice is too vague — the examiner wants to know, for example, that you would use the same volume of apple juice as the original vitamin C solution, that you would use the same concentration of DCPIP and so on. **4/6**

Student B

(a) There were slightly fewer men who had major cardiovascular events who took vitamin C than taking the placebo, ✓ but this difference is very small compared with the total number in the study ✓ so is almost certainly not significant. So we can say that taking vitamin C makes no difference. ✓

ⓔ A good answer, clearly expresssed. **2/2**

(b) (i) A very large number of people ✓ — 14641 — were used in the study.

ⓔ Correct. **1/1**

(ii) A placebo was given to one group and vitamin C to the other group, ✓ so there wasn't a variable of whether you took a pill or not. The people did not know which they were given. ✓
They were randomly assigned to the two groups, ✓ so this should avoid variables such as age or anything making a difference between the two sets of results.

ⓔ There are actually three correct answers here, because the point about the people not knowing whether they were given a placebo or not is different from the first point. **2/2**

(c) The data make it look as though people with a low BMI have more CVD than people with high BMI, but this is not right ✓ and it must be because there are more people in the study who actually have low BMI and fewer with high BMI. ✓ We need to know the percentage ✓ of people with low and high BMIs who have CVD, not just the numbers.

ⓔ Well explained. **3/3**

(d) Take some ascorbic acid and make it up into a solution of known concentration ✓ and put it into a flask. Put some DCPIP solution into a burette ✓ and drip it into the acid until it stays clear. Swirl it around while you are doing this to mix it in well. ✓ Record the volume of DCPIP used. ✓ Then put some apple juice into a clean flask ✓ and use the DCPIP still in the burette ✓ to record the volume that can be decolorised again. ✓ Do a calculation:

$$\text{concentration in apple juice} = \frac{\text{concentration in ascorbic acid solution} \times \text{volume of DCPIP used for apple juice}}{\text{volume of DCPIP used for ascorbic acid}} \checkmark$$

ⓔ All clear and correct, though ideally it should also say that you would use the same volumes of ascorbic acid solution and apple juice. **6/6**

Question 6

The diagram shows the double circulatory system of a mammal.

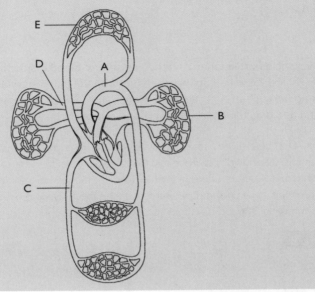

(a) **Give the letter of a structure that matches each of the following descriptions.**
   (i) **an artery containing deoxygenated blood**　　　　　　　　　　　(1 mark)
   (ii) **the place where blood is oxygenated**　　　　　　　　　　　　(1 mark)
   (iii)**a vessel that contains valves along its length**　　　　　　　(1 mark)
   (iv)**the vessel in which the blood is at its highest pressure**　　(1 mark)

(b) **Describe and explain what happens when the muscles in the walls of the ventricles
of the heart contract.**　　　　　　　　　　　　　　　　　　　(6 marks)

Total: 10 marks

ⓔ Note that (b) has *two* command words — 'describe' and 'explain'.

Student A

(a) (i) D ✓

ⓔ Correct. **1/1**

   (ii) E ✗

ⓔ Incorrect — student A has not looked carefully at the diagram but has just assumed that the
capillaries at the top are in the lungs. **0/1**

(iii) C ✓

ⓔ Correct. **I/I**

(iv) A ✓

ⓔ Correct. **I/I**

(b) The ventricles get smaller ✓ so the pressure of blood inside them gets bigger. ✓ So the blood is pushed up into the aorta and the pulmonary arteries. ✓ It can't go back up into the atria because the valves shut. The pressure in the arteries goes up and down as the heart contracts and relaxes.

ⓔ Student A has been given a mark for saying that the ventricles get smaller, but that is quite generous and he/she should really have said that the volume of the ventricles gets smaller. He/she has mentioned valves, but does not make clear which ones, nor why they shut. The statement about the pressure going up and down is irrelevant, as the question only asks what happens when the muscle contracts. **3/6**

<table>
<tr><td>Student B</td></tr>
</table>

(a) (i) D ✓

ⓔ Correct. **I/I**

(ii) B ✓

ⓔ Correct. **I/I**

(iii) C ✓

ⓔ Correct. **I/I**

(iv) A ✓

ⓔ Correct. **I/I**

(b) When muscle contracts it gets shorter, so this decreases the volume ✓ inside the ventricle and increases the pressure. ✓ Blood is forced upwards against the atrioventricular valves and shuts them ✓ so blood can't go up into the atria. ✓ Blood is also forced upwards against the semilunar valves in the arteries and opens them. ✓

ⓔ A better answer than student A, but it does not get full marks because it does not state which arteries the blood is pushed into. **5/6**

Question 7

In garden peas, seed colour may be green or yellow. This is determined by a gene with two alleles, G and g. Heterozygous peas are green.

(a) State which allele is dominant, and explain your answer.   (1 mark)

(b) Two heterozygous pea plants were bred together and produced 325 seeds. These were sown and allowed to grow into plants, of which 80 had yellow seeds and 245 had green seeds.
Construct a genetic diagram to explain these results.   (4 marks)

(c) Pea seeds contain stores of starch, which act as an energy reserve for the embryo. Explain why the molecular structure of starch makes starch suitable as an energy reserve.   (3 marks)

Total: 8 marks

ⓔ Genetic diagrams take time to write out fully, and it is tempting to take shortcuts. However, you really must do it properly, or you will lose marks.

Student A

(a) **G** because it has a capital letter. ✗

ⓔ Right allele but wrong reason! **0/1**

(b)   **Gg** × **Gg**

	G	**g** ✓
G	GG green	Gg green
g	Gg green	gg yellow ✓✓

ⓔ The genetic diagram is basically correct, but student A should really say what each set of symbols represents. The examiner has assumed that the letters around the square represent the gametes, but it would be much better if student A had said this, or at least put circles round them. The offspring genotypes and phenotypes are correct, but student A has not related these to the results of the experiment. **3/4**

(c) Starch is a polysaccharide so its molecules are very big ✓ and contain a lot of energy. It curls up into a ball so it doesn't take up too much space. ✓

ⓔ Two correct and relevant statements have been made. **2/3**

Student B

(a) G because when **Gg** are together the seeds are green, so **G** must be dominant and **g** recessive.

ⓔ Correct. **1/1**

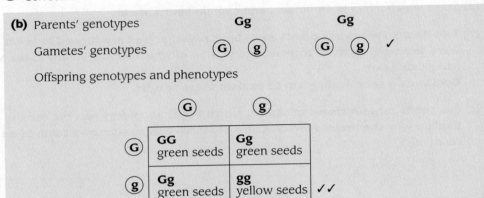

(b) Parents' genotypes   Gg   Gg

Gametes' genotypes   Ⓖ   ⓖ   Ⓖ   ⓖ   ✓

Offspring genotypes and phenotypes

	Ⓖ	ⓖ
Ⓖ	GG green seeds	Gg green seeds
ⓖ	Gg green seeds	gg yellow seeds

✓✓

This shows that we would expect 1/4 yellow seeds and 3/4 green seeds, which is approximately 80/325 and 245/325. ✓

ⓔ An entirely complete and correct genetic diagram, and an explanation of the results at the end. **4/4**

(c) Starch molecules are made of many glucose molecules ✓ linked in a chain by 1–4 glycosidic bonds. This makes it a good energy store because when it is needed it can be broken down to glucose ✓ which can be used in respiration to release energy. ✓ The molecules are very big so they don't dissolve in water ✓ and upset the workings of the cell.

ⓔ A good answer — student B could probably have said even more if there had been more marks available, but has been sensible and stopped when fairly sure he/she had enough to be worth at least 3 marks. **3/3**

Knowledge check answers

1 Carbon atoms 1 (on the left-hand molecule) and 4 (on the right-hand one).
2 Glycogen molecules are made of shorter chains of glucose molecules than starch molecules. Starch is actually a mixture of two substances — amylopectin and amylose — whereas glycogen is just a single substance. Amylose molecules curl up into a spiral, which glycogen does not do.
3 There are no parts of the lipid molecule that have charges on them, so they do not attract water molecules.
4 Time taken for one complete heart beat is about 0.75 seconds. (Look for the time from one particular part of the first heartbeat to the time for the same stage of the second one.) So in one minute there will be $60 \div 0.75 = 80$ beats.
5 All arteries carry blood away from the heart, but not all of them carry oxygenated blood. The pulmonary artery carries deoxygenated blood from the heart to the lungs.
6 The left side of the heart has more muscle in its wall. The contraction of this muscle produces a greater pressure than in the right side.
7 prothrombin, thrombin, fibrinogen, fibrin
8 Reducing high blood pressure reduces the likelihood of a blood vessel bursting, which could cause a stroke. It also reduces the risk of plaques forming in artery walls, which would make the wall less elastic and more likely to break when high-pressure blood surges through the vessel.
9 An example of a benefit: if you know you are at high risk of CVD, you can take action to reduce other risk factors. An example of a potential problem: insurance companies might want to know if you are at high or low risk, which could affect the premiums you have to pay. You will probably be able to think of many more possible advantages and disadvantages of having this knowledge.
10 $10\,cm^3$ of DCPIP were decolorised by $100\,cm^3$ of a $0.02\,g\,cm^{-3}$ ascorbic acid solution.
$10\,cm^3$ of DCPIP were decolorised by $250\,cm^3$ of the fruit juice.
So the concentration of ascorbic acid in the fruit juice is $(100 \div 250) \times 0.02 = 0.008\,g\,cm^{-3}$
You can also work this out by stating that it took 2.5 times as much fruit juice to decolorise the same amount of DCPIP, so it must have been 2.5 times less concentrated than the ascorbic acid solution. $0.02 \div 2.5 = 0.008\,g\,cm^{-3}$.
11 Two variables are said to be correlated if there is a relationship between them. For example, you may find that when one of them goes up, the other also goes up.
Causation means that a change in one variable actually *produces* a change in the other.
Just finding a correlation between two variables does not imply causation. There could be a third variable that is causing the change in both of them.
12 Water molecules have dipoles — that is, they have small positive and negative electrical charges on different parts of the molecule. These are attracted to opposite electrical charges on other molecules.
13 Breathing movements bring fresh supplies of air into the lungs. They remove air that is high in carbon dioxide and low in oxygen, and replace it with air that is low in carbon dioxide and high in oxygen. This maintains a diffusion gradient for both of these gases between the air in the alveoli and the blood.
14 They do both require energy input from the cell. In endocytosis, this is needed to put out the extensions and to cause the membrane to fuse to form a vacuole. In exocytosis, energy is needed to surround the object with membrane and to move it to the cell membrane.
15 The x-axis of your graph should be labelled 'temperature/°C', and have a scale of equal intervals running from 0 to 100. The y-axis should be labelled 'mean absorbance'. You don't know the units or the range here, so you could just put an upward-pointing arrow on the axis. The curve should start at about 0 and go upwards, levelling off at a fairly high temperature – this is because beyond a certain temperature the membrane will already be as leaky as it is going to get. You can't know exactly what this temperature will be, but 40°C would be a good guess.
16 A hydrogen bond is an attraction between two molecules caused by small positive and negative electrical charges on them.
17 Water molecules are attracted to the small charges on the R groups on the outside of the haemoglobin molecule. The water molecules therefore surround the haemoglobin molecule.
18 Broken hydrogen bonds mean that the enzyme molecule is no longer held in its correct 3D shape. The shape of the active site changes, so that the substrate molecule no longer fits. The enzyme loses its activity.
19 The axes for your curve should be labelled 'enzyme concentration/percentage concentration of initial solution' (x-axis) and 'mean volume of gas collected after 2 minutes/cm³' (y-axis). The curve will rise from 0 to a certain point and then level off.

20 RNA contains ribose, while DNA has deoxyribose.
RNA contains uracil, while DNA has thymine.
RNA is single-stranded, while DNA is made of two strands.

21 ^{15}N atoms contain one more proton than ^{14}N, so they have a greater mass. This means that DNA containing ^{15}N is heavier than DNA containing ^{14}N.

22 If conservative replication had taken place, then we would get no DNA that had a mixture of ^{15}N and ^{14}N. All the 'old' DNA would contain only ^{15}N, so we would always get a narrow band of DNA in the base of the tube, as for the first result. All of the 'new' DNA would contain only ^{14}N, so we get a second band higher up the tube, with no 'middle' band.

23 The anticodon of three bases on a tRNA molecule determines which amino acid it will pick up. This anticodon then binds with its complementary codon on the mRNA molecule, ensuring that the correct amino acid is brought to add to the chain.

24 The lost amino acid might have an R group that is important in forming bonds that help to hold the protein molecule in its correct 3D shape. If the protein molecule loses its shape, it may not be able to function correctly.

25 Allele for smooth seeds: **A**
Allele for wrinkled seeds: **a**

Parents' genotypes	Aa		Aa	
Gametes' genotypes	(A) (a)		(A) (a)	

Offspring genotypes and phenotypes

	Female gametes	
	(A)	(a)
Male gametes (A)	AA smooth seeds	Aa smooth seeds
(a)	Aa smooth seeds	aa wrinkled seeds